Second Edition

Foundations of Mathematics for Virginia

Guided Notebook

Acknowledgements

Thank you to the entire developmental mathematics department at Germanna Community College in Virginia for their work and development of these resources. Individual efforts of writing, reviewing, and sharing ideas resulted in a great team product. A special thank you to Catherine Jackson who spearheaded and championed the project.

Tara Cantwell
Robin J. Coppock*
Trina L. Campbell*
Theresa Cooper
Martha Crigler
Stacie T. Ferry*
Anwar Haj
Linda Holland*
Catherine Jackson*
Sanjeeva Kanth
Connie Kronander
Patricia M. Parker*
Andria L. Powell Ross*
Kim Riddle
Rebecca J. Triana*
Rae A. Rich Van Vranken

*Project Writers

Editor:
Kara Roché

Creative Director:
Tee Jay Zajac

Designers:
Trudy Gove,
Patrick Thompson,
Tee Jay Zajac

Cover Design:
Trudy Gove

VP Research & Development: Marcel Prevuznak

Director of Content: Kara Roché

A division of Quant Systems, Inc.

546 Long Point Road
Mount Pleasant, SC 29464

Printed in the United States of America

10 9 8 7 6 5 4 3 2

ISBN: 978-1-64277-046-9

Table of Contents

Unit 3

Algebra Basics

Unit 4

First Degree Equations and Inequalities in One Variable

Unit 5

Linear Equations, Inequalities, and Systems of Linear Equations in Two Variables

Unit 6

Exponents, Factoring and Polynomial Equations

Unit 7

Rational Expressions and Equations

Unit 8

Roots, Radicals, and Complex Numbers

Unit 9

Functions, Quadratic Equations, and Parabolas

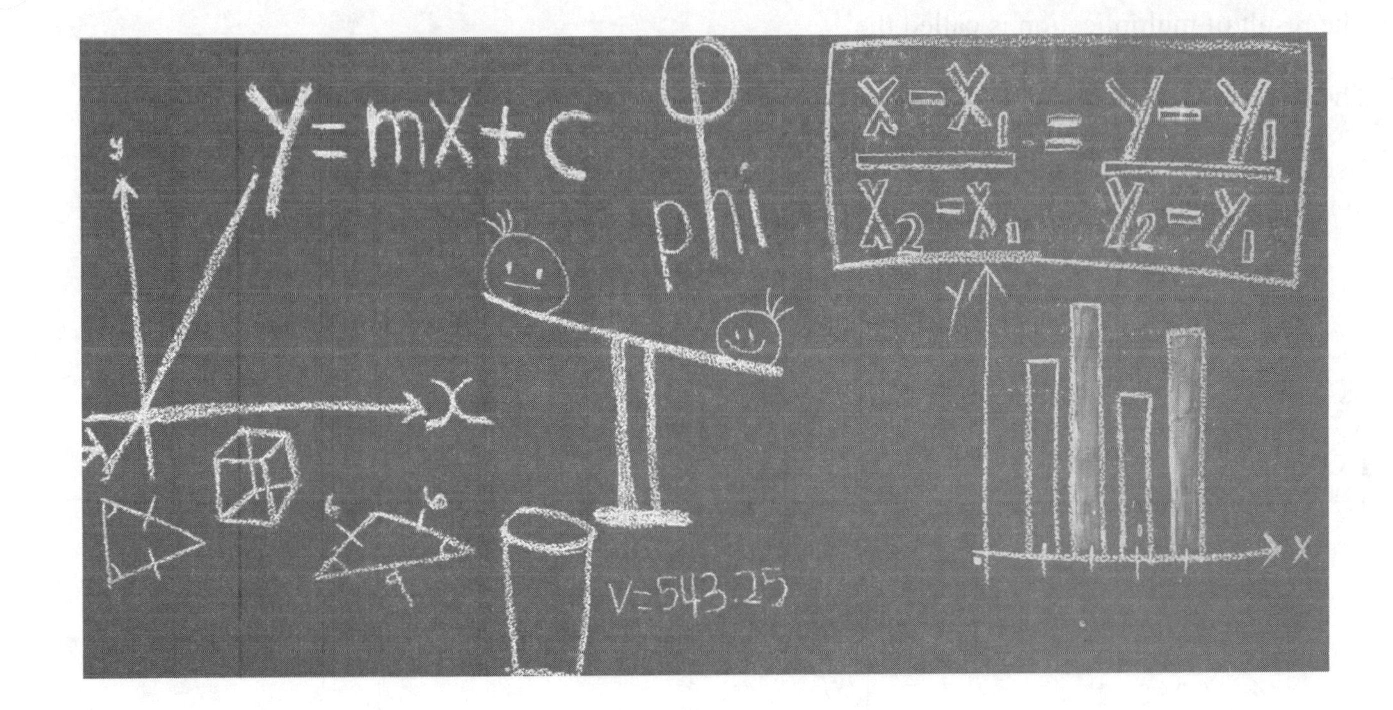

Unit 1

Operations with Fractions

Exponents and Prime Numbers

The result of multiplication is called the ______________.

The type of operation used when working with exponents is repeated ________________.

Use these terms (**repeated multiplication, base, exponent, exponential expression, product**) to label each number or numbers in the following:

$$3 \cdot 3 \cdot 3 \cdot 3 \quad = \quad 3^4 \quad = \quad 81$$

Examples

1. Complete the table below.

	Repeated Multiplication	Exponential Form	Value
a.	$5 \cdot 5$	5^2	25
b.	$2 \cdot 2 \cdot 2$		
c.		5^3	
d.			10,000

2a. $8^2 = 64$ is read as____

b. $5^3 = 125$ is read as____

c. $2^5 = 32$ is read as____

What is meant by the **factors** of a number?

Define **prime numbers**.

Define **composite numbers**.

Examples

3. Give a few examples of prime numbers and list their factors.

4. Give a few examples of composite numbers and list their factors.

List all the prime numbers less than 50. You should recognize these in the future as prime.

Which number is the only even prime number?

Except for the number 2, all prime numbers are odd, but not all odd numbers are prime. List some examples to justify this statement.

Steps for finding the prime factorization of a composite number.

1.

2.

3.

Examples

Find the prime factorization for each of the following numbers. Write the factorization using exponents. If a number is prime, then write "prime."

5. 90 6a. 65 b. 72 c. 294

Tests for Divisibility

If a number is divisible by 2, it will end in ______________________.

If a number is divisible by 3, the digits will add up to a number divisible by ______.

If a number is divisible by 5, it will end in ____________.

If a number is divisible by 6, it will be divisible by both _______ and ________.

If a number is divisible by 9, the digits will add up to a number divisible by ________.

If a number is divisible by 10, it will end in _______.

Quick Quiz

Rewrite the following products using exponents.

1. $5 \cdot 5 \cdot 5 \cdot 7 \cdot 7$

2. $2 \cdot 3 \cdot 3 \cdot 11 \cdot 11$

Find an exponential expression for each of the following numbers without using the exponent 1.

3. 125

4. 81

Evaluate.

5. 2^4

6. 3^3

Find the prime factorization of each number. If the number is prime, write prime.

7. 128

8. 630

9. 43

Introduction to Fractions and Mixed Numbers

Define a **fraction** and identify its parts.

Examples

1a. If a whole pizza is cut into 3 equal pieces, then 2 of these pieces represent what fraction of the pizza?

1b. In a rectangle, 3 of the 4 equal parts are shaded.
What fraction represents the shaded parts?
What fraction represents the unshaded parts?

Define **proper fraction**.

List some examples of proper fractions.

Define **improper fraction**.

List some examples of improper fractions.

$\frac{5}{5}$ is considered an improper fraction because its value is ≥ 1. Use of improper fractions in mathematical computations and answers are appropriate unless indicated or you are answering an application most often communicated in mixed numbers.

Examples

2. Draw a circle and shade 5 out of 6 equal parts.

3. Draw a picture that illustrates the improper fraction $\frac{5}{3}$.

How do you write a whole number, like 4, in fraction form?

The number 0 in fractions.	
$\frac{0}{\#} = 0$	$\frac{\#}{0} = \text{undefined}$

What does it mean for an answer to be undefined?

Examples

4a. $\frac{0}{36} =$ b. $\frac{0}{124} =$ c. $\frac{17}{0} =$ d. $\frac{1}{0} =$

Steps to reduce fractions to lowest terms.

1.

2.

Examples

Reduce each fraction to lowest terms.

5a. $\frac{15}{20}$ b. $\frac{4}{36}$ c. $\frac{35}{21}$

What is your answer if all of the factors in the numerator or denominator reduce or divide-out?

Examples

Reduce each fraction to lowest terms.

6. $\frac{44}{20}$ 7. $\frac{52}{65}$

Steps to change a mixed number into an improper fraction.

1.

2.

3.

Examples

Change each mixed number to an improper fraction.

8. $8\frac{9}{10}$ 9. $11\frac{2}{3}$

Steps to change an improper fraction to a mixed number.

1.

2.

Examples

10. Change $\frac{67}{5}$ to a mixed number.

When working with mixed numbers, a final answer should not include both a whole number and an improper fraction. You can resolve this by using either of the following methods.

- Change the mixed number to an improper fraction and then change it back to a mixed number using the procedures above.
- Turn the improper part of the answer into a mixed number and add it to the original whole number.

Reduce the mixed number $6\frac{5}{4}$ so that the fraction is not improper.

Quick Quiz

Reduce each fraction to lowest terms.

1. $\frac{24}{10}$ 2. $\frac{16}{32}$ 3. $\frac{24}{1}$ 4. $\frac{4}{0}$

Change each number to an improper fraction.

5. $3\frac{2}{7}$ 6. $4\frac{3}{4}$ 7. 7

Change each number to a mixed number.

8. $\frac{25}{8}$ 9. $\frac{43}{7}$

Rewrite the number in appropriate mixed number form.

4. $3\frac{7}{2}$

5. If you had \$20 and you spent \$9 for a hamburger, fries, and a soft drink…
   a. What fraction of your money did you spend?
   b. What fraction of your money did you have left over?

Ratios and Rates

Define **ratio**:

Show three ways a ratio can be written.

List three characteristics of ratios.

1.

2.

3.

Examples

1. Compare the quantities 40 desks and 30 students as a ratio.

2a. Write the comparison of 2 feet to 3 yards as a ratio.

b. Write the ratio as an abstract number in all 3 ways.

The word "per" means "divided by."

What is the procedure for changing rates to unit rates?

Examples

3. A bicyclist rides at a steady speed over level ground for 26 miles in 2 hours. Find her speed in miles per hour. (**Note: values differ from Learn, answer 13 mph**)

4. Find the rate of a frog hopping across a road if the road is 40 feet wide and the frog hops 10 times to get across the road.

5. You find yourself reading a particularly exciting novel about Native Americans during the early 1800s. In one afternoon in the library, you read 300 pages of this book in 2 hours. What was your rate of reading? That is, how many pages did you read in one hour? **(Note: values differ from Learn, answer 150 pages/hour)**

6. A candy shop is selling 18 pieces of candy for 90 cents. A competitor candy shop is selling 15 pieces of the same candy for 60 cents. Which is the better buy?

7. At the local Shop and Save grocery store, tubs of ice cream come in 3 different sizes. Find the price per pint for each size and tell which is the best buy.

   a. 2 pints for $8.00 b. 4 pints for $12.00 c. 7 pints for $14.00

Quick Quiz

Write each comparison as a ratio or rate reduced to lowest terms.

1. 75 miles to 3 gallons of gas
2. 20 cats to thirty dogs
3. 140 minutes to 3 hours (Hint: 60 min = 1 hr)
4. 2 dimes to 2 quarters (Hint: think "cents")
5. 100 cm to 1 m (Hint: 1 m = 100 cm)
6. About 28 out of every 100 African-Americans have type A blood. Express this fact as a ratio in lowest terms.
7. John has collected 7 quarters while Walt has collected 25 dimes. How much money does Walt have compared with John's accumulation?

Multiplication and Division with Fractions and Mixed Numbers

Steps to multiply fractions.

1.

2.

The word "**of**" means multiply.

Examples

1. Find $\frac{2}{5}$ of $\frac{7}{3}$.

2. Multiply and reduce if necessary.

a. $\frac{4}{13} \cdot 3$ b. $\frac{9}{8} \cdot 0$ c. $4 \cdot \frac{5}{3} \cdot \frac{2}{7}$

Product is the answer when two numbers are _______________.

Change mixed numbers to improper fractions when multiplying or dividing.

Examples

3. Find the product $1\frac{1}{2} \cdot 2\frac{1}{5}$.

4. Find $\frac{3}{5}$ of $5\frac{3}{4}$.

When multiplying fractions, it is possible to reduce before multiplying by dividing the numerators and denominators by common factors. Reducing in this way is sometimes called dividing-out or cancelling.

What happens if all the factors in the numerator or denominator divide-out?

Examples

Multiply and reduce to lowest terms.

5. $\frac{15}{28} \cdot \frac{7}{9}$

6. $\frac{9}{10} \cdot \frac{25}{32} \cdot \frac{44}{33}$

7. $\frac{55}{26} \cdot \frac{8}{44} \cdot \frac{91}{35}$

8. $4\frac{2}{3} \cdot 1\frac{1}{7} \cdot 2\frac{1}{16}$

9. $\frac{9}{10} \cdot \frac{25}{64} \cdot \frac{8}{3}$

10. $\frac{36}{49} \cdot \frac{14}{75} \cdot \frac{15}{18}$

11. A study showed that $\frac{5}{8}$ of the members of a public service organization were in favor of a new set of bylaws. If the organization had a membership of 200 people, how many were in favor of the changes in the bylaws?

What is a **reciprocal**?

What is the reciprocal of 0?

Examples
State the reciprocal of each.

12. $\frac{2}{3}$

13. 10

Steps to divide fractions.

1. Change any mixed numbers to improper fractions.
2. Change division to ______________________.
3. Flip the ____________________ fraction.
4. Then we can ____________________ and reduce.

The result of a division problem is called the **quotient**.

Examples
Divide and reduce to lowest terms.

14. $\frac{3}{4} \div \frac{2}{3}$

15. $\frac{16}{27} \div \frac{8}{9}$

16. $\frac{16}{27} \div 2\frac{8}{9}$

17. $3\frac{1}{4} \div 19\frac{1}{2}$

18. If the product of $1\frac{1}{2}$ and another number is $\frac{5}{18}$, what is the other number?

19. A box contains 30 pieces of candy. This is $\frac{3}{5}$ of the maximum amount of candy the box can hold.
    a. Is the maximum amount of candy the box can hold more or less than 30 pieces?
    b. If you want to multiply $\frac{3}{5}$ times 30, would the product be more or less than 30?
    c. What is the maximum number of pieces of candy the box can hold?

Quick Quiz

Perform the indicated operations. Reduce all answers.

1. $2\frac{2}{5} \cdot 3\frac{1}{4}$

2. $1\frac{6}{8} \cdot 1\frac{1}{4}$

3. $\frac{5}{6} \cdot \frac{3}{5}$

4. $\frac{3}{4} \cdot \frac{5}{6} \cdot \frac{4}{15}$

5. $\frac{10}{13} \div \frac{5}{26}$

6. $\frac{2}{3} \div 4$

7. $2\frac{1}{17} \div 1\frac{1}{4}$

8. $1\frac{1}{32} \div 2\frac{3}{4}$

9. $\frac{12}{13} \div 0$

10. The product of two numbers is 150. If one number is $\frac{5}{7}$, what is the other?

11. Major League Baseball teams play 162 games each season. If a team has played $\frac{5}{9}$ of its games by the All-Star break, how many games has it played by that time?

Least Common Multiple

What is a **multiple**?

List the multiples of 8 (up to 100):

List the multiples of 12 (up to 100):

Define **least common multiple** (LCM).

List the steps to find the LCM.

1.

2.

3.

Examples

1. Find the LCM of 20 and 45. Show your work.

20 45 LCM = ________________ = _______

2. Find the LCM of 12, 18, and 48. Show your work.

12 18 48 LCM = ________________ = _______

What is the difference between the greatest common factor and the least common multiple?

Examples

Find the LCM of each set of numbers.

3. 36, 24, and 48

4. 27, 30, and 42

5. 8 and 25

Examples 6 and 7 illustrate how to use prime factorizations to tell how many times each number in a set will divide into the LCM. Use this helpful method to do the following.

6. Find the LCM for 27, 30, and 42; then state how many times each number divides into the LCM.

7. Find the LCM for 12, 18, and 66; then state how many times each number divides into the LCM.

8. Suppose it takes three weather satellites—A, B, and C—different lengths of time to orbit the Earth. Satellite A takes 24 hours, B takes 18 hours, and C takes 12 hours. If they are directly above each other now, as shown in their beginning positions in the figure, in how many hours will they again be directly above each other as shown in their beginning positions? How many orbits will each satellite have made in that time? See the illustration provided in Learn.

We can create an equivalent fraction by multiplying or dividing the numerator and the denominator by the same nonzero factor.

Examples

Find the missing numerator that will make the fractions equivalent.

9. $\frac{3}{4} = \frac{?}{28}$ 10. $\frac{9}{10} = \frac{?}{30}$ 11. $\frac{3}{5} = \frac{?}{55}$

Quick Quiz

Find the LCM of each group of numbers.

1. 22 and 40
2. 10, 12, and 48

Find the missing numerator that will make the fractions equal.

3. $\frac{2}{5} = \frac{?}{25}$
4. $\frac{8}{9} = \frac{?}{36}$

5. During an 8 hour day, John can make 4 flower arrangements, Sally can make 7, and Luis can make 3.
   a. Find the LCM of the number of flower arrangements each worker can make in an 8 hour day.
   b. What is the smallest number of 8 hour days needed for each of them to make the same number of arrangements?

6. Three swimmers decide to swim laps together and they will quit when they reach the starting end of the pool all together at the same time. The first swimmer can swim a lap in 35 seconds, the second will take 40 seconds, and the third takes 42 seconds.
   a. How many seconds will it take before they quit?
   b. How many laps did each swimmer swim during this time interval?

Addition and Subtraction with Fractions

Steps for adding and subtracting fractions.
(Summarize the steps here after working the examples, make sure to address what to do with both the numerator and denominator.)

1.

2.

3.

4.

The result of an addition problem is called the **sum**.
The result of a subtraction problem is called the **difference**.

Examples
Find the sum.

1. $\frac{1}{5}+\frac{2}{5}$

2. $\frac{4}{15}+\frac{6}{15}$

3. $\frac{1}{11}+\frac{5}{11}+\frac{3}{11}$

4. $\frac{3}{8}+\frac{13}{12}$

5. $\frac{7}{45}+\frac{7}{36}$

6. $\frac{2}{3}+\frac{1}{6}+\frac{5}{12}$

Caution: We cannot reduce first when adding or subtracting. That method only applies to multiplication and division.

Show the correct way to add $\frac{3}{2}+\frac{1}{6}$.

Examples

7. Rachel is mailing two letters at the post office. One letter weighs $\frac{1}{3}$ ounces and the other weighs $\frac{3}{7}$ ounces. What is the combined weight of the letters?

8. If Keith's total income for the year was $36,000 and he spent $\frac{1}{4}$ of his income on rent and $\frac{1}{12}$ of his income on his car, what total amount did he spend on these two items?

Find each difference.

9. $\frac{9}{10} - \frac{7}{10}$

10. $\frac{7}{8} - \frac{3}{8}$

11. $\frac{9}{10} - \frac{2}{15}$

12. $\frac{7}{20} - \frac{3}{28}$

13. $\frac{11}{12} - \frac{13}{20}$

14. The Narragansett Grays baseball team lost 90 games in one season. If $\frac{1}{5}$ of their losses were by 1 or 2 runs and $\frac{4}{9}$ of their losses were by 3 or fewer runs, what fraction of their losses were by exactly 3 runs?

Quick Quiz

Perform the indicated operation. Reduce if possible.

1. $\frac{4}{15}+\frac{1}{15}$

2. $\frac{1}{10}+\frac{3}{100}$

3. $\frac{16}{25}-\frac{11}{25}$

4. $\frac{5}{6}-\frac{4}{15}$

5. $\frac{7}{10}-\frac{41}{100}$

6. $\frac{2}{5}+\frac{4}{35}+\frac{7}{15}$

7. Three pieces of mail weigh $\frac{1}{2}$ ounces, $\frac{1}{5}$ ounces, and $\frac{3}{10}$ ounces. What is the total weight of the letters?

8. Sam's income is $3300 a month and he plans to budget $\frac{1}{3}$ of his income for rent and $\frac{1}{10}$ of his income for food. What amount of money does he plan to spend each month on these two items?

Addition and Subtraction with Mixed Numbers

A mixed number is the sum of a whole number and a fraction.

Steps to add or subtract mixed numbers.

1.

2.

3.

Examples

Find the sum.

1. $\begin{array}{r} 5\frac{2}{9} \\ +\ 8\frac{5}{9} \\ \hline \end{array}$

2. $35\frac{1}{6} + 22\frac{7}{18}$

3. $\begin{array}{r} 5\frac{3}{4} \\ 9\frac{3}{10} \\ +\ 2 \\ \hline \end{array}$

Find the difference. (Be sure to pay attention to the denominators.)

4. $\begin{array}{r} 10\frac{3}{7} \\ -\ 6\frac{2}{7} \\ \hline \end{array}$

5. $\begin{array}{r} 13\frac{4}{5} \\ -\ 7\frac{1}{3} \\ \hline \end{array}$

When will you have to "borrow" from the whole number?

Find the difference.

6. $\begin{array}{r} 6 \\ -\ 2\frac{1}{3} \\ \hline \end{array}$

7. $\begin{array}{r} 76\frac{5}{12} \\ -\ 29\frac{13}{20} \\ \hline \end{array}$

8. $\begin{array}{r} 4\frac{2}{9} \\ -\ 1\frac{5}{9} \\ \hline \end{array}$

Borrowing can be avoided if we change mixed numbers to improper fractions before finding the common denominator.

Repeat numbers 7 and 8 above using this method.

Which method did you prefer for number 7? How about for number 8?

Quick Quiz

Simplify the following mixed numbers.

1. $5\frac{5}{4}$

2. $10\frac{13}{7}$

Perform the indicated operation. Reduce if possible.

3. $6\frac{1}{7}+2\frac{3}{7}$

4. $3\frac{4}{5}+\frac{7}{20}$

5. $6\frac{1}{12}+2\frac{3}{8}+1\frac{2}{3}$

6. $9\frac{7}{12}-2\frac{5}{18}$

7. $4\frac{3}{8}-2\frac{7}{8}$

8. $12\frac{1}{2}-5\frac{5}{6}$

9. $9-7\frac{5}{8}$

10. A triangle has sides that measure $42\frac{3}{4}$ feet, $23\frac{1}{2}$ feet, and $22\frac{7}{8}$ feet. Find the perimeter of the triangle.

Order of Operations with Fractions and Mixed Numbers

Steps to compare fractions.

1.

2.

3.

Examples

1. Which is larger $\frac{5}{6}$ or $\frac{7}{8}$? How much larger?

2. Which is larger $\frac{8}{9}$ or $\frac{11}{12}$? How much larger?

3. Arrange $\frac{2}{3}$, $\frac{7}{10}$, and $\frac{9}{15}$ in order from smallest to largest.
Then find the difference between the smallest and the largest.

Rules for Order of Operations: PEMDAS

1.

2.

3.

4.

If there are 6 letters in the mnemonic PEMDAS, why do we list them as four steps for solving problems?

PEMDAS is a mnemonic device that may help you remember the order of operations. Another popular one is "Please Excuse My Dear Aunt Sally's Last Remarks" which stands for Parenthesis, Exponents, Multiply or Divide, Add or Subtract – Left to Right. Perhaps you have made up your own for recalling the steps?

Examples

Evaluate each of the following.

4. $\frac{1}{2} \div \frac{3}{4} + \frac{5}{6} \cdot \frac{1}{5}$

5. $\frac{9}{10} - \left(\frac{1}{4}\right)^2 + \frac{1}{2}$

6. $\frac{3}{5} \div \frac{1}{4} \cdot \frac{1}{2} + \left(\frac{1}{3}\right)^2$

7. $\left(\frac{7}{8} - \frac{7}{10}\right) \div \frac{7}{2}$

8. $3\frac{2}{5} \div \left(\frac{1}{4} + \frac{3}{5}\right)$

9. $\left(5\frac{2}{3} - 2\frac{1}{3}\right) \div \left(1\frac{1}{2} + 1\right)$

10. $2\frac{1}{2} \cdot 1\frac{1}{6} + 7 \div \frac{3}{4}$

Steps to find the average of a set of numbers.

1.

2.

When you have a fraction divided by a fraction, this is called a complex fraction. You can rewrite a complex fraction using the ÷ sign to separate the numerator and denominator of the big fraction.

For example: $\frac{\frac{2}{3}}{\frac{4}{5}}$ is the same as $\frac{2}{3} \div \frac{4}{5}$.

This may come in handy as you do the next problem.

Examples

11. Find the average of $1\frac{1}{2}$, $2\frac{3}{4}$, and $3\frac{5}{8}$.

Quick Quiz

Arrange the numbers in order from smallest to largest.

1. $\frac{5}{6}, \frac{3}{4}, \frac{9}{10}$

2. $\frac{3}{8}, \frac{5}{16}, \frac{17}{32}$

Evaluate each expression using the order of operations.

3. $\frac{3}{20} \cdot \frac{5}{7} \div \frac{1}{4} - \frac{3}{14} \cdot \frac{2}{3}$

4. $\frac{1}{3} - 1\frac{1}{2}\left(2 - \frac{2}{3}\right)^2$

5. $\frac{1\frac{2}{5} - \frac{3}{5}}{\frac{1}{2} + \frac{2}{3}}$

6. Find the average of $3\frac{1}{2}$, $4\frac{2}{3}$, and $1\frac{1}{5}$.

Vocabulary Check

Define each of the following terms in your own words, providing examples as necessary to clarify the term.

Average

Base

Complex Fraction

Composite Number

Denominator

Difference

Equivalent Fraction

Exponent

Factor

Fraction

Improper Fraction

Least Common Multiple

Numerator

Order of Operations

Prime Factorization

Prime Number

Product

Proper Fraction

Quotient

Ratio

Reciprocal

Sum

Concept Review

Answer the following questions as completely as possible in your own words. Make sure to get the big points of each with key steps involved.

1. How do you find the LCM of two numbers?

2. How do you find the LCD of two or more fractions?

3. How do you simplify or reduce a fraction?

4. What are the steps for adding/subtracting fractions?

5. What are the steps for multiplying fractions?

6. What are the steps for dividing fractions?

7. How do you change a mixed number to improper fraction and vice versa?

8. How do you find the prime factorization of a given number?

9. Given two fractions, how can you determine which one is <, > or =?

10. What is PEMDAS used for and when do you use it?

11. How do you change between two units of customary units of measurement?

12. What makes a fraction undefined?

13. With fractions, which operations require a common denominator?

14. With fractions, which operations cannot be done using mixed numbers?

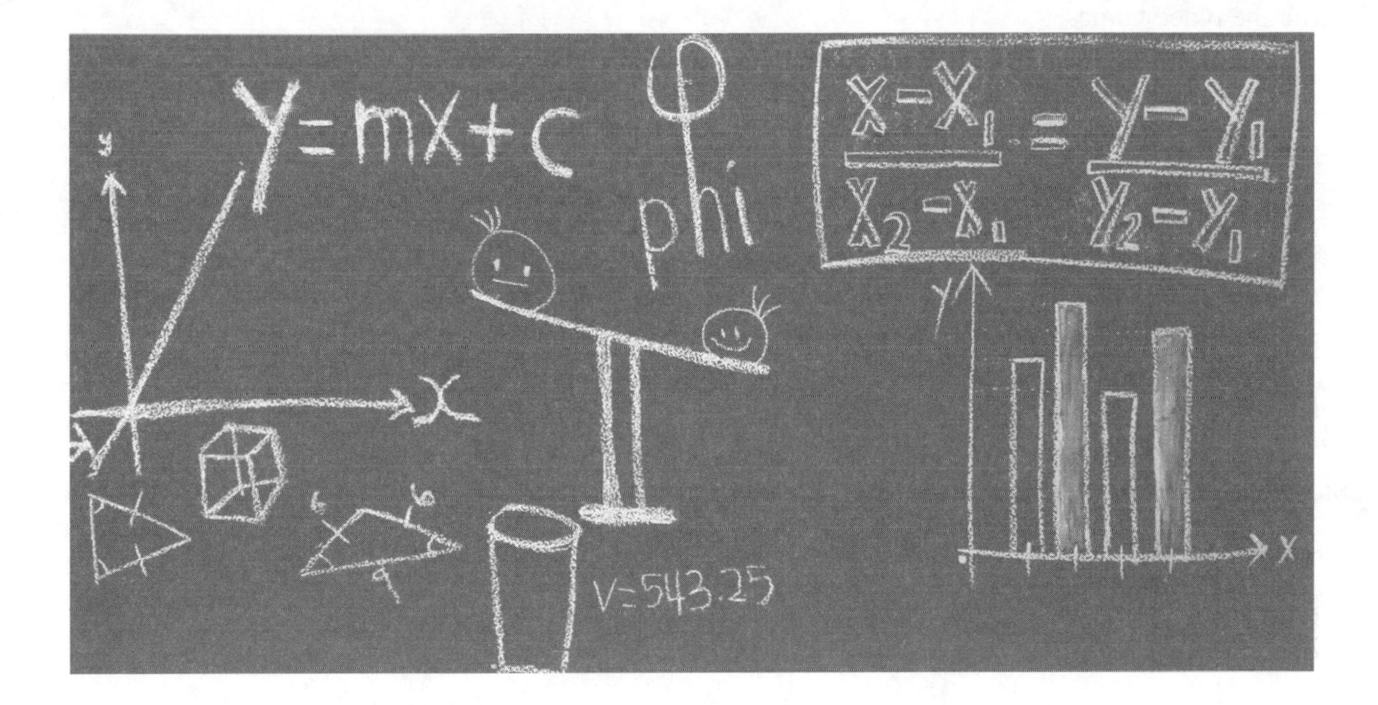

Unit 2

Operations with Decimals and Percents

Introduction to Decimal Numbers

Write the place values.

				• Decimal point				

Notice the "**th**" at the end of these, indicating a fraction part.

We do not use commas on the right side of the decimal to separate different place value groups as we often do on the left side.

Steps to read or write a decimal number.

1.

2.

3.

Examples

1. Write the mixed number $48\frac{6}{10}$ in decimal notation.

   And in words.

2. Write the mixed number $12\frac{75}{10000}$ in decimal notation.

   And in words.

3. Write "four hundred **and** two thousandths" in decimal notation.

4. Write "four hundred two thousandths" in decimal notation.

Steps to compare two decimal numbers.

1.

2.

Examples

Which number is larger?

5. 3.126 or 3.14

6. 0.08 or 0.085

7. Write the following numbers in order, smallest to largest: 6.37, 5.14, 6.28

Rules for rounding decimal numbers.

1.

2.

3.

4.

Examples

Round each number to the place value given.

8. 18.649 to the nearest tenth

9. 5.83971 to the nearest thousandth

10. 2.00643 to the nearest ten-thousandth

11. 9653 to the nearest hundred

Quick Quiz

Round each number to the given place value.

1. 16.753 to the nearest tenth

2. 1359.26436 to the nearest thousandth

3. 5.04567 to the nearest ten-thousandth

4. 7382.147 to the nearest hundred

Write the following decimal numbers in their English word equivalent.

5. 125.7

6. 4.758

Write the given number in standard notation.

7. Two hundred and fifteen thousandths

8. Two hundred fifteen thousandths

Addition and Subtraction with Decimal Numbers

Steps to add or subtract decimal numbers.

1.

2.

3.

4.

Examples

Find the sum for each of the following:

1. $6.3 + 5.42 + 14.07$

2. $9 + 4.86 + 37.479 + 0.6$

3. $56.2 + 85.75 + 29.001$

4. Mrs. Finn went to the local store and bought a pair of shoes for \$42.50, a blouse for \$25.60, and a skirt for \$37.55. How much did she spend? (Tax was included in the prices.)

Find the difference.

5. $16.715 - 4.823$

6. $21.2 - 13.716$

In Hawkes Learning, when asked to estimate, round to the **leftmost** nonzero digit unless a specific place value is indicated. Sometimes when estimating in your daily life, you may find it helpful to round to other place values.

7a. Estimate the sum. $74 + 3.529 + 52.61$

b. Find the actual sum.

Quick Quiz

Find the sum or difference.

1. $3.72 + 8.309 + 6.2$

2. $17.3 + 125.17 + 88.625$

3. $43.67 - 5.8$

4. $182.359 - 23.46$

5a. Estimate the sum. $56.19 + 83.72$

b. Find the actual sum.

Multiplication with Decimal Numbers

Steps to multiply decimal numbers.

1.

2.

3.

When multiplying numbers vertically, the numbers are written atop each other – there is no need to line up the decimals. Other methods of multiplication like the Lattice Method can be used when multiplying decimal numbers as well.

Examples
Multiply.

1. 2.432×5.1 2. 4.35×12.6 3. $(0.046)(0.007)$ 4. 3.4×5.8

Steps to multiply a decimal number by a power of 10.

1.

2.

Examples

5. Multiply each by simply <u>moving the decimal</u> the appropriate number of places.

a. $(1.59) \times 10$ b. $(2.68) \times 100$ c. $(0.9653) \times 1000$

d. $(7.2) \times 1000$ e. $(3.5149) \times 10^2$

Estimating products can be done by rounding each number to the place of the last nonzero digit on the left. Again, sometimes in your daily life you may round to a different place value while estimating depending on the level of accuracy you desire.

Examples

6a. Estimate the product. (0.356)(6.1)

b. Find the actual product.

7. You can buy a car for $15,000 cash or you can make a down payment of $3750 and then pay $1093.33 each month for 12 months. How much can you save by paying cash?

Why would we NOT round 12 to 10?

Quick Quiz

Multiply.

1. 8.57×6.2

2. 3.621×2.85

3. (0.059) (.003)

4. $(7.583)(10^3)$

5a. Estimate (0.3624) (8.3)

b. Find the exact answer.

Division with Decimal Numbers

Steps to divide decimal numbers.

1.

2.

3.

4.

Examples

1. Find the quotient. 63.86 ÷ 6.2

2. Divide. 24.225 ÷ 4.25

If you are dividing two numbers and the remainder is NOT zero, i.e. one number does not go in evenly to the other, how can you finish the division and give your answer as a fraction? How about finishing the division and giving your answer as a decimal?

How do you know how many zeros to add as you continue to divide two numbers and not get a remainder of 0 in the process?

Examples

Find the quotient to the place given.

3. 82.3 ÷ 2.9 to the nearest tenth

4. 1.83 ÷ 4.1 to the nearest hundredth

If multiplying a number by a power of 10, moving the decimal one unit to the right for each multiple of 10, what will happen if we divide by a power of 10?

Steps to divide a decimal number by a power of 10.

1.

2.

Examples
5. Divide the following by simply moving the decimal the appropriate number of places.

a. $5.23 \div 100$ b. $817 \div 10$ c. $495.6 \div 10^3$ d. $286.5 \div 10^2$

When estimating, remember to round each number to the place of the last nonzero digit on the left.

Examples
6a. Estimate the quotient. $6.2 \div 0.302$ b. Find the actual quotient (to tenth).

Order of Operations: [PEMDAS]

1.

2.

3.

4.

If there are 6 letters in the mnemonic PEMDAS, why do we list them as four steps for solving problems?

PEMDAS is a mnemonic device that may help you remember the order of operations. Another popular one is "Please Excuse My Dear Aunt Sally's Last Remarks" which stands for Parenthesis, Exponents, Multiply or Divide, Add or Subtract – Left to Right. Perhaps you have made up your own for recalling the steps?

Examples

Apply the order of operations to find the value of the expression.

7. $(3.1)^2 + 7.05 \div 1.5$

8. $2.1(45.2 - 10.8) - 15.38$

How do you find the **average amount per unit**?

Examples

9. The gas tank of a car holds 17 gallons of gasoline. Estimate how many miles per gallon the car averages if it will go 470 miles on one tank of gas.

10. If you ride your bike at an average speed of 15.2 miles per hour, how far will you ride in 3.5 hours?

11. The price of a gallon of gas at the pump is $3.15, including tax. If the tax you pay on each gallon of gas is 0.45 times the original price of a gallon of gas, what is the price of a gallon of gas before tax (to the nearest penny)?

Quick Quiz

Divide.

1. $146.19 \div 0.03$

2. $74.325 \div 2.5$

3. $123.48 \div 2.74$ (nearest hundredth)

4. $192.41 \div 3.6$ (nearest hundredth)

5. Compute. $(3.17 + 6.93)^2 - 2.64 \div 2.2$

6. A quarter section of beef can be bought cheaper than the same amount of meat purchased a few pounds at a time. Estimate the cost per pound if 150 pounds costs $187.50. What is the actual cost per pound?

Decimal Numbers and Fractions

Steps to change a decimal number to a fraction.

1.

2.

Examples

Change each decimal number to a reduced fraction.

1. 0.25 2. 0.32 3. 0.131 4. 0.075

5. Change 2.6 to a reduced fraction and then to a reduced mixed number.

6. During baseball season, major league players' batting averages are published in the newspapers. If a player has a batting average of 0.250, what does this indicate?

What is a **terminating decimal**?

What is a **nonterminating decimal**?

To change a **fraction to a decimal**, divide the numerator by the denominator.

Examples

Change each fraction to a decimal number.

7. $\frac{3}{8}$ 8. $\frac{5}{4}$

What is a **repeating decimal**?

Examples

9. Change $\frac{7}{12}$ to a decimal number rounded to the nearest thousandth.

10. Change $\frac{3}{22}$ to a repeating decimal.

11. Change each addend to decimal form, then find the sum. $10\frac{1}{2} + 7.32 + 5\frac{3}{5}$

12. Determine whether $\frac{3}{16}$ is larger than 0.18 by changing $\frac{3}{16}$ to decimal form and then comparing the two numbers. Then find the difference.

Quick Quiz

1. Change 0.625 to a reduced fraction.

2. Change 5.8 to a reduced fraction and then to a reduced mixed number.

3. Change $\frac{7}{8}$ to a decimal number.

4. Change $\frac{4}{27}$ to a repeating decimal.

5. Order from smallest to largest. $\frac{5}{18}, 0.267, \frac{2}{9}$

Decimal Numbers and Percents

The word "percent" comes from the Latin *per centum*, meaning per hundred.

Examples

1. Write each fraction as a percent.

a. $\frac{7}{100}$ b. $\frac{83}{100}$ c. $\frac{64}{100}$ d. $\frac{100}{100}$ e. $\frac{240}{100}$

How do you change a **decimal to a percent**?

1.

2.

Examples

2. Write each decimal number as a percent.

a. 0.253 b. 0.905 c. 2.65 d. 0.01 e. 0.002

How do you change a **percent to a decimal**?

1.

2.

Examples

3. Change each percent to an equivalent decimal number.

a. 76% b. 18.5% c. 50% d. 100% e. 0.25%

Quick Quiz

1. Write $\frac{5.3}{100}$ as a percent.
2. Write 0.765 as a percent.
3. Change 57% to a decimal.
4. Change $\frac{7}{8}$ to a percent.
5. Change 83% to a decimal.
6. Change $\frac{12}{100}$ to a decimal.
7. Fill in the missing values in the tables. Reduce all fractions to lowest terms.

Fraction	Decimal	Percent
	0.12	
		$\frac{3}{8}\%$

Fraction	Decimal	Percent
$1\frac{9}{16}$		
	2.34	
		30%

Fractions and Percents

What are the steps to change a **fraction to a percent**?

1.

2.

To multiply by a mixed number, we must first change the mixed number to an improper fraction. For example: $2\frac{1}{4} = \frac{2 \cdot 4 + 1}{4} = \frac{9}{4}$

Examples

1. Change $\frac{5}{8}$ to a percent.

2. Change $2\frac{1}{4}$ to a percent.

When a decimal number is long and therefore is often rounded, how can we represent the exact value of that number?

Examples

3. Change $\frac{1}{3}$ to a percent.

a. Round to the nearest tenth of a percent.

b. Give the exact percent.

4. During the years 1921 to 2005, the New York Yankees baseball team played in 39 World Series Championships and won 26 of them. What percent of these championships did the Yankees win?

a. Round to the nearest tenth of a percent.

b. Give the exact percent.

How do you change a **percent to a fraction**?

1.

2.

Examples

Change each percent to a fraction.

5. 60%

6. 130%

If you eat $\frac{1}{2}$ of a pie and your friend eats $\frac{1}{2}\%$ of a pie, have you eaten the same amount? Justify your answer by showing the two values' equivalency or that they are not equal.

Then try these… Are the given values in A and B equal? If no, why not?

A Convert to a decimal	B Convert to a decimal	Are the two values equal?
$\frac{1}{4}\%$	$\frac{1}{4}$	
$12\frac{1}{2}\%$	$12\frac{1}{2}$	

Write the list of common percent-decimal-fraction equivalents here and work to memorize them.

Quick Quiz

1. Change $\frac{11}{20}$ to a percent.

2. Change 62.5% to a reduced fraction.

3. Betty pays income tax of 24% on her pay from working as a labor and delivery nurse. Express 24% as a fraction reduced to lowest terms.

4. The portfolio of an investor increased by 385%. Express this as a mixed number reduced to lowest terms.

Solving Proportions

Define **proportion**.

How do we determine if a proportion is true?

Examples

1. Use the cross product technique to determine whether each proportion is true or false.

a. $\frac{6}{8} = \frac{15}{20}$ b. $\frac{5}{8} = \frac{7}{10}$ c. $\frac{9}{13} = \frac{4.5}{6.5}$

2. Determine whether the proportion is true or false. $\frac{2\frac{1}{3}}{7} = \frac{3\frac{1}{4}}{9\frac{3}{4}}$

Steps to solve a proportion.

1.

2.

3.

Examples

Solve the proportion.

3. $\frac{3}{6} = \frac{5}{x}$

4. $\frac{3}{8} = \frac{y}{2.4}$

To divide by a fraction, we multiply by its reciprocal.

5. Find A if $\frac{A}{7} = \frac{20}{\frac{2}{3}}$

6. $\frac{2\frac{1}{2}}{6} = \frac{3}{y}$

Steps to solve a word problem by using a proportion.

1.

2.

3.

Examples

7. A motorcycle will travel 352 miles on 11 gallons of gas. How many miles will this motorcycle travel on 15 gallons of gas?

8. An architect draws the plans for a building by using a scale of $\frac{1}{2}$ inch to represent 10 feet. How many feet does 6 inches represent?

9. A recommended mixture of weed killer is 3 capfuls for 2 gallons of water. How many capfuls should be mixed with 5 gallons of water?

Quick Quiz

Determine if the proportion is true or false.

1. $\frac{8\frac{7}{2}}{2\frac{1}{3}} = \frac{4\frac{1}{4}}{1\frac{1}{6}}$ 2. $\frac{6}{8} = \frac{15}{20}$ 3. $\frac{3}{4} = \frac{25}{20}$ 4. $\frac{4}{5} = \frac{2.4}{3}$

5. Solve. $\frac{y}{371} = \frac{26}{182}$ 6. Solve. $\frac{y}{7} = \frac{21}{49}$

7. If property taxes are figured at $1.50 for every $100 in valuation, what taxes will be paid on a home valued at $85,000?

U.S. Measurements

If you needed to know how many tablespoons are in a cup and didn't happen to have a math book handy, where would you look to find this equivalency? List 3-4 ways you could find this information – including some without the use of technology.

Examples

1. Complete.

a. 1 gal = ____ qt b. 3 ft = ____ yd c. 60 min = ____ hr

d. 1 T = _____ lb

Steps to convert from one size unit to another using multiplication or division.

1.

2.

Converting units of measures can be done in several different ways. During this unit, focus on applying the concept of proportions to convert between two units. You will get the same answer using other methods appropriately as well. The first example shows the use of proportions to convert between cups and fluid ounces.

Examples

2. Convert each of the given units to the desired units.

a. 3 c = ______ fl oz

$$\frac{3\text{ cups}}{1\text{ cup}} = \frac{x\text{ fl oz}}{8\text{ fl oz}}$$

now cross multiply to solve for x.

b. 5 gal = _______ qt

c. 150 min = _______ hr

d. 39 in. = ________ ft

Steps for using unit fractions to convert measures.

1.

2.

Examples

3. Use unit fractions to convert measures.

a. 21 ft =_____ yd

b. 15 hr = ______ min

c. $6\frac{1}{2}$ qt = ______ pt

d. 40 oz = ______ lb

4. Some conversions take two steps. Convert each unit.

a. 3520 yd = _________ miles

b. 6 gal = _______ pt

Some units of measure are mixed units (almost like mixed numbers). For example, hours and minutes, pounds and ounces, feet and inches. When converting make sure to identify the units of each numerical value in the solution.

Examples

5. Converting measures with a remainder

a. 136 min = _____ hr ____ min

b. 2 T 89 lb = ________ lb

If you are adding and subtracting mixed units, what do you do if the smaller unit has more value than its conversion factor? For example, 4 hours and 82 minutes.

Adding and subtracting measures

6a.
```
   3 hr  15 min
+  2 hr  50 min
```

b.
```
  14 lb   8 oz
−  6 lb  13 oz
```

Quick Quiz

Convert.

1. 5 min = ______ sec

2. 48 in. = _______ ft

3. 7 yd = _______ ft

4. 32 fl oz = _______ c

5. Perform the indicated operation.
14 lb 8 oz + 5 lb 11 oz = _______ lb _______ oz

The Metric System

The Metric System differs from the U.S. system in that all of its units are based on units of 10. This provides a consistent relationship between units of measurement by using prefixes representing powers of 10 in front of the base unit: meter, gram, or liter.

Knowing the order of the metric system prefixes helps identify the size of items and to convert between units. One mnemonic device is below. The "unit" stands for meter, liter, or gram. You might have one of your own or would like to make one up.

King	Henry	Doesn't	Usually	Drink	Chocolate	Milk
Kilo-	Hecto-	Deka-	Unit	Deci-	Centi-	Milli-

What type of measurements do each of the metric units measure?
A meter is a measure of ________________.
A gram is a measure of ________________.
A liter is a measure of ________________.

To convert between units in the metric system, the proportion method learned previously will work as well. But there is a shorter way! Why can we convert between units in the metric system simply by moving the decimal?

How do you convert between two units of metric measure? How do you know which way to move the decimal?

Examples

Convert between the given units of measure.

1a. 5.6 m = ___________ cm

b. 5.6 m = ____________ mm

c. 23.5 cm = _____________ mm

d. 1.42 km = _____________ m

2a. 375 cm = _____ m

b. 375 mm = ________ m

c. 1055 m =_________ km

3. Change to 56 cm to meters.

4. Change 13.5 m to millimeters.

In the metric system,

- A 0 is written to the left of a decimal point if there is no whole number part (0.287 m) to help protect the decimal from being dropped or going unnoticed.
- No commas are used in writing numbers. For a number with many digits, a space can be inserted between each group of 3 digits counting from the decimal in either direction. (This is not a practice commonly used in our daily communication.)

Examples

5a. 23 mg = ________ g

b. 6 g = ________ mg

c. 49 kg = ________ g

6a. 60 mg = ________ g

b. 135 mg = ________ g

c. 100 g = ________ kg

d. 78 kg = ________ g

If we represented each of these units physically, it would look like this:

1 cm — Length – 1 dimensional

1 cm^2 — Area – 2 dimensional

1cm^3 — Volume – 3 dimensional

If we know that there are 100 cm in every meter and wanted to draw 1 meter in terms of centimeters, how many centimeters would we draw in a line?
What if we wanted to draw 1 m^2 in terms of centimeters, how many centimeters would it take to fill the square?
What if we wanted to draw 1 m^3 in terms of centimeters, how many centimeters would it take to fill the cube?

If we summarize what we just learned, we develop the following relationships that connect to converting squared and cubic units in general.

1 m = 100 cm	To convert – move 2 decimal places (x100)	1 dimensional – move 2 units ONCE (length)
1 m^2 = 10000 cm^2	To convert – move 4 decimal places (x10000)	2 dimensional – move 2 units TWICE (length and width)
1 m^3 = 1000000 cm^3	To convert – move 6 decimal places (x1000000)	3 dimensional – move 2 units TRIPLE (length, width, and height)

To convert **AREA** measurements, we move the decimal **twice** for every unit change to represent the two dimensions.

To convert **VOLUME** measurements, we move the decimal **triple** for every unit change to represent the three dimensions.

Examples

7a. $15\ cm^3$ = __________ mm^3 b. $4.1\ dm^3$ = __________ cm^3

c. $8\ dm^3$ = __________ m^3 d. $22.6\ m^3$ = __________ cm^3

8a. $3.7\ dm^3$ = __________ cm^3 b. $0.8\ m^3$ = __________ dam^3

c. $4\ m^3$ = __________ dm^3 = __________ cm^3 = __________ mm^3

9a. 6 L = __________ mL = __________ hL b. 500 mL = __________ L

c. 3 kL = __________ L d. 72 hL= __________ kL

10a. 6000 mL = __________ L b. 3.2 L = __________ mL

c. 60 hL = __________ kL d. 637 mL = __________ L

Table 5: Equivalent Measures of Volume

1 mL =1 cm^3
1 L = 1 dm^3
1 kL = 1 m^3

What does this mean? Draw a picture of 1 cubic centimeter. (1 cm^3) If centimeters is a measure of length and milliliters is a measure of liquid volume, then how can 1 mL = 1 cm^3?

Are you becoming a nurse or entering a medical field or have you ever tried to give a small child medication and didn't recognize the units? Take a look at a medicine spoon and compare the difference between a "cc" or mL and a tsp. The term "cc" stands for cubic centimeters.

$$1\ cc = 1\ cm^3 = 1\ mL$$

Examples

10e. 70 mL = __________ cm^3 f. 3.8 kL = __________ m^3

When completing computations of values with units, all units must be the same in order to add or subtract. If multiplying or dividing by a constant, the answer will keep the original units.

Examples (Be aware of units!)

11a. 4 g + 13 g b. 12 cm – 2 mm c. 3 mL x 7 d. 54 kg ÷ 6

Something to think about… Has the U.S. ever considered converting to the metric system? Why do you think we have not converted?

Quick Quiz

Convert as indicated.

1. 18.25 m = _______ dm
2. How many centimeters are in 3.2 mm?
3. Express 896 grams in milligrams.
4. 8.7 m^3 = _______ cm^3
5. 80 L = _______ mL = _______ cm^3
6. 3 m + 15 cm = _______ m

U.S. to Metric Conversions

Understanding the relationship between units of U.S. measurement and units of metric measurement is important not only because of international commerce but because we sometimes communicate and/or travel to other countries. We also use many metric systems in our day to day business in the U.S. Ask your auto mechanic the next time you take the car in if he or she uses the metric system.

Temperature
What are the two units of measurement for temperature? Which one is customarily used in the U.S.? What do the two units have in common?

Examples

1. How hot or cold is it? Describe each pair of temperature values in words that will give you reference to how hot or cold that temperature feels.

$100°C = 212°F$ $40°C = 104°F$ $20°C = 68°F$

Formulas for Converting Temperatures	
$C = \frac{5(F - 32)}{9}$	$F = \frac{9C}{5} + 32$

2. Convert 86°F to Celsius.

3. Convert 40°C to Fahrenheit.

Converting between U.S. and Metric Units

Fill in the table below of equivalent values for each conversion. Think about how each compares size wise as you do. Which unit is bigger or smaller?

Length Equivalents	
U.S. to Metric	Metric to U.S.
1 in. =	1 cm =
1 ft =	1 m =
1 yd =	1 m =
1 mi =	1 km =

Area Equivalents	
U.S. to Metric	Metric to U.S.
1 in.^{2} =	1 cm^2 =
1 ft^2 =	1 m^2 =
1 yd^2 =	1 m^2 =
1 mi^2 =	1 km^2 =
1 acre = (hectare)	1 ha =

Volume Equivalents	
U.S. to Metric	Metric to U.S.
1 in.^{3} =	1 cm^3 =
1 ft^3 =	1 m^3 =
1 qt =	1 L =
1 gal =	1 L =

Mass Equivalents	
U.S. to Metric	Metric to U.S.
1 oz =	1 g =
1 lb =	1 kg =

Remember m = meters and mi = miles.

How do you think the equivalents between metric and U.S. units were found? Why are they estimates?

Why does the table include both U.S. to Metric and Metric to U.S.? When a measurement is given 1 in. = 2.54 cm versus 1 cm = 0.394 in., even though these are extremely close to being the same, the first equivalency started with 1 inch and estimated how many centimeters it took to cover that 1 inch. In reverse, if we start with 1 centimeter, it will take only 0.394 of an inch to cover that centimeter. Therefore it is slightly more accurate to use the conversion table that matches your direction of conversion.

Let's test this out. Using proportions and the conversion factor given, find the value for the new unit. How close are the two answers? Which one would be more accurate?

Given 23 inches, convert this to centimeters using the equivalency provided.	
Use 1 in. = 2.54 cm	Use 1 cm = 0.394 in.

How do you convert between any two units of measure using proportions?

Examples

Convert the given value to the new unit.

4. 6 ft = _____ cm

5. 25 mi = ____ km

6. 30 m = ____ ft

7. 10 km = ____ mi

8. 40 yd^2 = ____ m^2

9. 5 acres = ____ ha

10. 5 ha = ____ acres

11. 100 cm^2 = _____ $in.^2$

12. 20 gal = ____ L

13. 42 L =_____ gal

14. 6 qt = _____ L

15. 10 cm^3 = ____ $in.^3$

16. 5 lb = ______ kg

17. 15 kg = ______ lb

Something to think about… Ever wonder why we buy milk by the gallon and soda by the liter?

Quick Quiz

1. Change 41˚F to degrees Celsius.

2. How many inches are in 50 cm?

3. Convert 100 feet to meters.

4. Suppose that the home you are considering buying sits on a rectangular shaped lot that is 270 ft by 121 ft. Convert this area to square meters

Reading Graphs

What is a **graph**? How can a graph help convey the message you are trying to send?

Describe the purpose for each type of graph. (Draw a sample of each one after describing its purpose.)
1. Bar Graphs

2. Circle Graphs

3. Line Graphs

4. Histograms

The properties of all graphs:

1.

2.

3.

What do you want to consider when you decide what graph to use to display information?

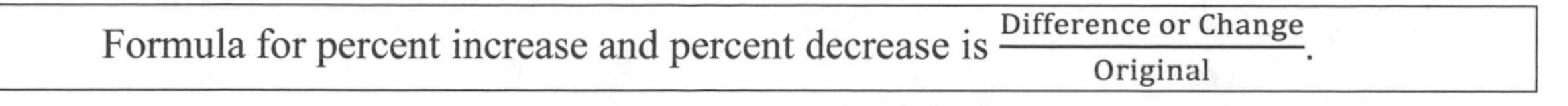
Formula for percent increase and percent decrease is $\frac{\text{Difference or Change}}{\text{Original}}$.

Examples

Use the graphs to answer the following questions.

1a. What were the sales in January? (Note the scale on the left of the graph.)

b. During what month were sales lowest?

c. During what month were sales highest?

d. What were the sales during each of the highest sales months?

e. What were the sales in April?

f. What was the amount of decrease in sales between February and March?

g. What was the **percent of decrease** in sales from February to March?

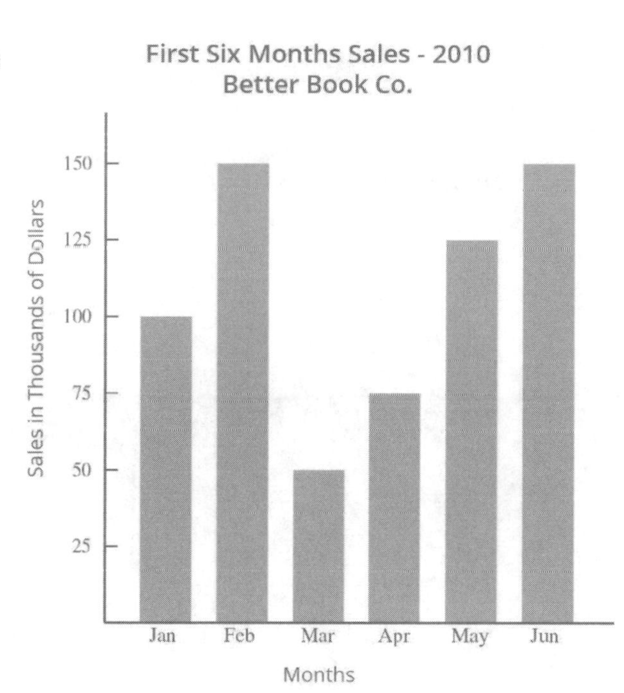

2. Calculate what amount of money will be allocated to each item indicated if the family income was $45,000.

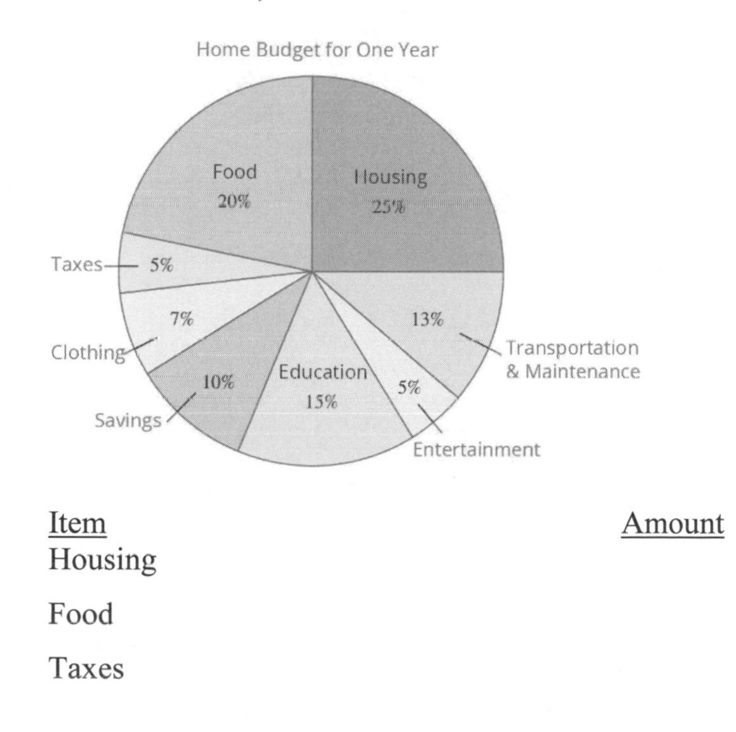

<u>Item</u> <u>Amount</u>

Housing

Food

Taxes

Clothing

Savings

Education

Entertainment

Transportation and Maintenance

3. Calculate the percentage of the total family income for each category.

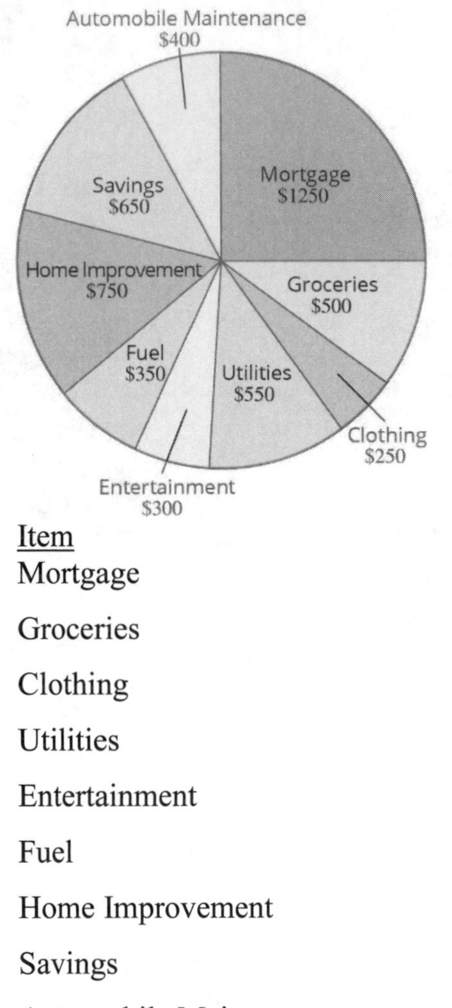

Item	Percentage
Mortgage	
Groceries	
Clothing	
Utilities	
Entertainment	
Fuel	
Home Improvement	
Savings	
Automobile Maintenance	

4. Calculate the differences between the high and low temperatures for each day.

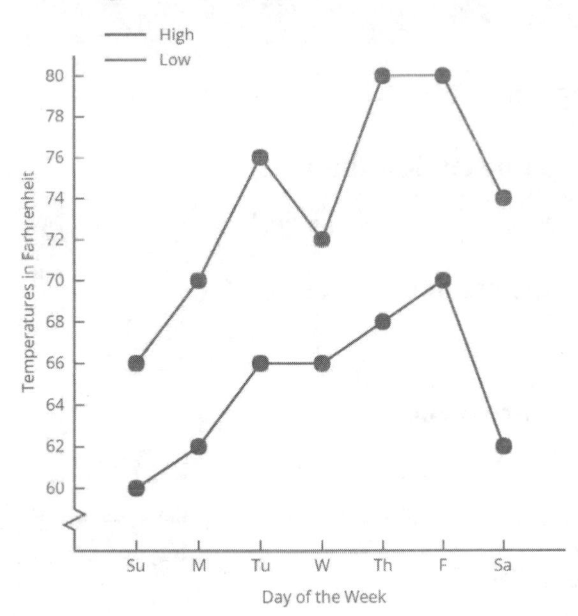

Day	Difference
Sunday
Monday
Tuesday
Wednesday
Thursday
Friday
Saturday

Find the mean (average) of the differences to find the average daily change in temperature for the week.

What is the difference between a bar graph and a histogram?

Define each of the terms below as related to histograms.

Class:

Lower class limit:

Upper class limit:

Class boundaries:

Class width:

Frequency:

Examples

5. Use the histogram to answer the following questions.

a. How many classes are represented?

b. What are the class limits of the first class?

c. What are the class boundaries of the second class?

d. What is the width of each class?

e. Which class has the greatest frequency?

f. What is this frequency?

g. What percent of the scores are between 200.5 and 250.5?

h. What percent of the scores are above 400.5?

Quick Quiz

A monthly income of $2800 is budgeted as shown. Find the amount of money budgeted for the given category.

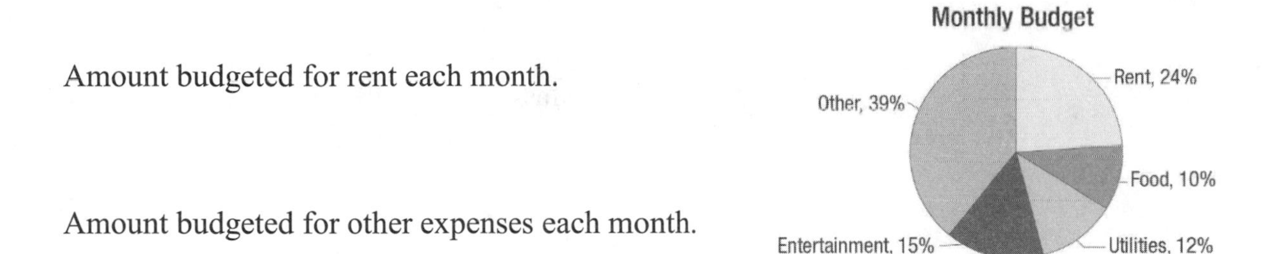

1. Amount budgeted for rent each month.

2. Amount budgeted for other expenses each month.

3. Amount budgeted for food and entertainment each month.

4. Total amount budgeted for all categories excluding other expenses.

The histogram shows prices for a one-bedroom apartment near Charleston, SC.

5. How many classes are represented?

6. What is the width of each class?

7. How many apartments total are in the data set?

8. Which class has the highest frequency?

Vocabulary Check

Define each of the following terms in your own words, providing examples as necessary to clarify the term.

Average

Bar graph

Celsius

Circle graph

Decimal notation

Dividend

Divisor

Fahrenheit

Gram

Histogram

Kilogram

Line graph

Liter

Mass

Meter

Nonterminating decimal

Percent

Powers of 10

Proportion

Quotient

Remainder

Terminating decimal

Unit fraction

U.S. Customary System

Volume

Weight

Concept Review

Answer the following questions as completely as possible in your own words. Make sure to get the big points of each with key steps involved.

1. What do the following words mean?
   a. Sum

   b. Difference

   c. Product

   d. Quotient

2. How do you write the answer to a division problem if there is something left over? (i.e. a remainder without using the R for remainder)

3. What is the order of operations and how do you apply it?

4. How do you order decimals?

5. What are the names of each decimal place?

6. When adding or subtracting decimals, what must you line up?

7. When you multiply decimals, what do you line up?

8. What do you do with the decimal in the product when multiplying?

9. What do you do with the decimal when dividing?

10. How do you change:
    a. A fraction to a decimal

    b. A decimal to a percent

    c. A percent to a fraction

d. A percent to a decimal

e. A decimal to a fraction

f. A fraction to a percent

11. How do you change between two units of customary units of measurement?

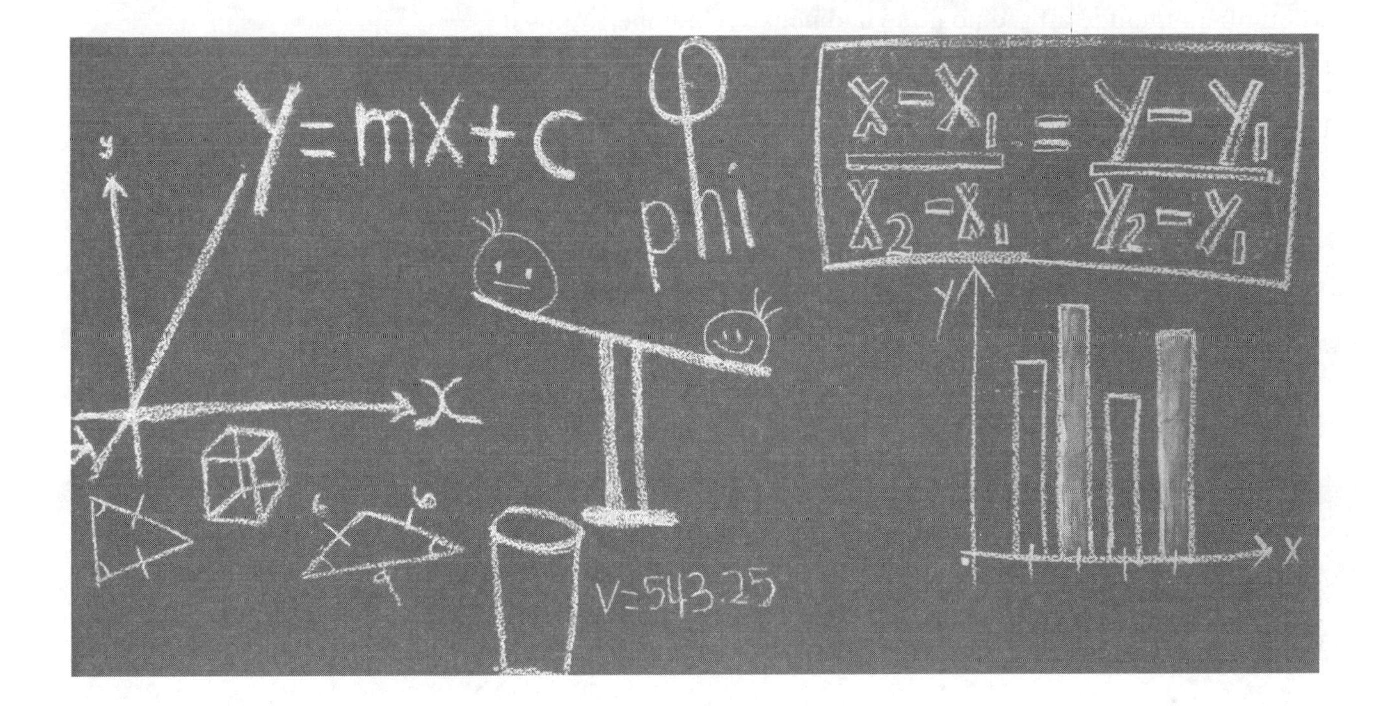

Unit 3

Algebra Basics

The Real Number Line and Inequalities

Real numbers include all the positive and negative numbers, plus 0.

> **The Negative Sign**
> The negative sign (−) in front of a number can be read three different ways depending on the context.
> The number −3 is read as "negative 3" or the "opposite of 3".
> The number −3 when behind another number such as 5−3 is read as "five minus three" but the 3 is still considered a negative value.

Describe what numbers each classification includes:

Integers: { ______________________________ }

Positive Integers: { ______________________________ }

Negative Integers: { ______________________________ }

> Notice that Zero is Neither Positive Nor Negative. Zero is its own opposite.

Concept Check

1. The opposite of an integer is always negative. True or False
2. The opposite of 0 is undefined. True or False

Examples

1a. State the opposite of 7. b. State the opposite of -4.

2a. Graph the set of integers $\{-3, -1, 1, 3\}$ ⟵————————⟶

b. Graph the set of integers $\{-6, -5, -4, -3\}$ ⟵————————⟶

⟵ **Real Numbers** ⟶

Irrational Numbers	**Rational Numbers**		
Non-repeating pattern Non-terminating decimals (often generated by a square root of a non-perfect square)	**Fractions** Ratio of 2 numbers	**Integers** {…−2, −1, 0, 1, 2…} **Whole Numbers** {0, 1, 2, 3…} **Natural Numbers** {1, 2, 3...}	**Decimals** Repeat or terminate

Examples

3. List the numbers in the set $S = \{-5, -\frac{3}{4}, 0, \sqrt{2}, 17\}$ that are…

a. Whole numbers

b. Integers

c. Rational numbers

d. Real numbers

Smaller numbers are always located to the **left** of larger numbers on a number line.

$<$ is read ______________________ $>$ is read ______________________

$\leq$ is read ______________________ $\geq$ is read ______________________

$=$ is read ______________________

Examples

4. Determine whether each of the following statements is true or false.

$7 < 15$ $3 > -1$ $4 \geq -4$ $2.7 \geq 2.7$ $-5 < -6$

Notice that $2.7 \geq 2.7$ is true. This is because we read "2.7 is greater than **OR** equal to 2.7". The word "OR" indicates that **only one thing has to be true** to make the statement true.

5a. Graph the set of real numbers. $\{-\frac{3}{4}, 0, 1, 1.5, 3\}$

b. Graph the Natural numbers less than or equal to 3.

Quick Quiz

Insert the correct symbol ($<$, $>$, $=$, $\leq$, $\geq$).

1. 7 ______ 10 2. −4 ______ −2 3. 8 ______ −8

Circle the rational numbers.

4. $-\frac{3}{4}$ 16 π 0 5.9

Circle the irrational numbers.

5. −4 7 −9.3 π 0 $\frac{1}{4}$

Introduction to Absolute Value

The **absolute value** of a real number is its distance from ___________. The absolute value of a real number is NEVER _____________ because the measurement of distance is always positive.

A negative would be giving a direction not the actual distance. Your distance from school to home and home to school are the same, a positive value.

Examples

1a. $|6.3| =$ ____________ b. $-|-2.9| =$ _____________

2. True or False: $|-4| \geq 4$ Why?

3a. If $|x| = 7$, what are the possible values for x?

b. If $|x| = -3$, what are the possible values for x?

Quick Quiz

Graph each set of real numbers on a real number line.

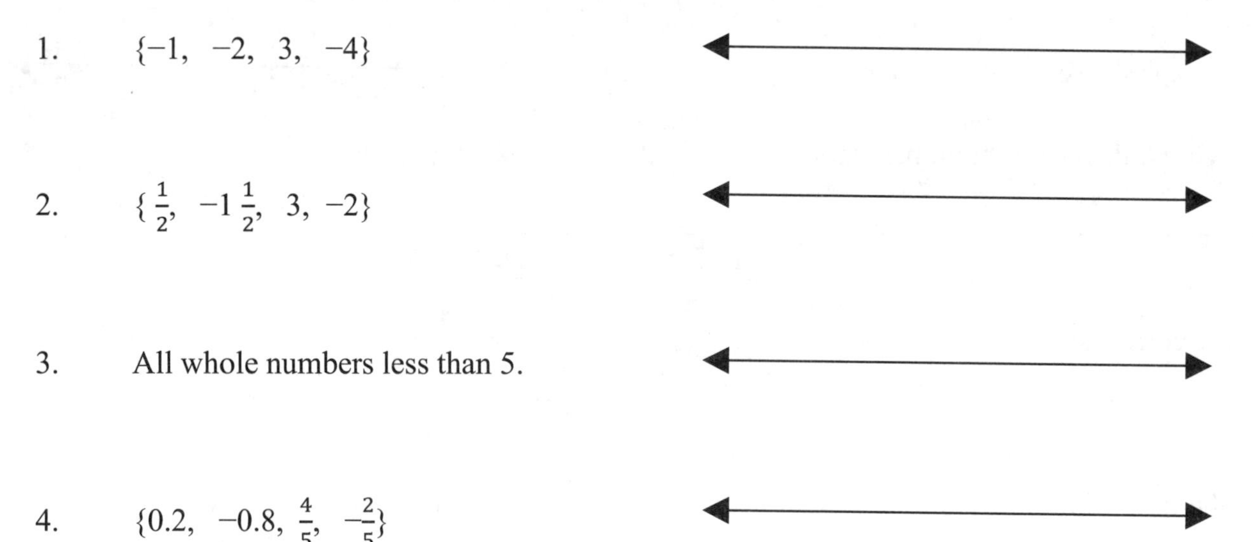

1. $\{-1, -2, 3, -4\}$

2. $\{\frac{1}{2}, -1\frac{1}{2}, 3, -2\}$

3. All whole numbers less than 5.

4. $\{0.2, -0.8, \frac{4}{5}, -\frac{2}{5}\}$

Introduction to Exponents

Define an **exponent**.

In the example below label each part as to what it represents.

$$5^3 \quad = \quad 5 \cdot 5 \cdot 5 \quad = \quad 125$$

Examples

1. In each exponential expression identify the base and the exponent.
   a. 6^2 b. 10^4

2. a. $8^2 = 64$ is read:

   b. $6^3 = 216$ is read:

   c. $5^4 = 625$ is read:

3. Rewrite each expression in exponential form and then evaluate the expression:
   a. $7 \cdot 7$ b. $2 \cdot 2 \cdot 2$ c. $2 \cdot 2 \cdot 2 \cdot 2 \cdot 2$

If no exponent is shown, it is understood to be 1. $a = a^1$ or $6 = 6^1$

4a. $9^1 =$ ________ b. $10^1 =$ ________

Rules for **Order of Operations**: PEMDAS

1.

2.

3.

4.

Examples

Evaluate.

5. $14 \div 7 + 3 \cdot 2 - 5$

6. $(6 + 2) + (8 + 1) \div 9$

7. $2 \cdot 3^2 + 18 \div 3^2$

8. $30 \div 10 \cdot 2^3 + 3(6 - 2)$

9. $2[5^2 + (2 \cdot 3^2 - 10)]$

10. $3(2 + 2^2) - 6 - 3 \cdot 2^2$

Quick Quiz

Evaluate each exponential expression.

1. 2^5

2. 3^4

3. $(-4)^3$

4. -9^2

Square Roots

If an integer is squared, the result is called a _______________ _________________.

$\sqrt{\ }$ is called the __________________ ___________.

The number under the radical sign is called the ____________________.

The complete expression, such as $\sqrt{49}$, is called the _______________.

List all the perfect squares up to 400. Work to recall these quickly as well as the base that generated the value.

Examples

1. Find the square roots:
   a. $\sqrt{100}$ b. $\sqrt{169}$ c. $-\sqrt{121}$ d. $-\sqrt{361}$

2. Find the value of each of the expressions:
   a. $(\sqrt{81})^2$ b. $(\sqrt{25})^2$ c. $(\sqrt{3})^2$

3. The $\sqrt{2}$ is between what two integers? Use a calculator to find its exact value.

4. The $\sqrt{18}$ is between what two integers? Use a calculator to find its exact value.

Quick Quiz

Find the square root of each number.

1. 49
2. 121
3. The $\sqrt{53}$ is between what two integers?
4. The $\sqrt{8}$ is between what two integers?

Addition with Real Numbers

Rules for Addition

The sign(s) in front of the number belong to that number. (Signs same, number + and signs different, number −)
If the signs are the SAME, we find the SUM of the absolute values.
If the signs are DIFFERENT, we find the DIFFERENCE of the absolute values.
Then use the sign of the number with the largest absolute value for the answer.

Examples

Find the value of each numerical expression. Remember a LCD is needed with fractions.

1a. $(10) + (3)$ b. $(-10) + (-3)$ c. $(-1.4) + (-2.5)$

d. $\left(\frac{3}{4}\right) + \left(\frac{1}{3}\right)$

2a. $(-10) + (3)$ b. $(10) + (-3)$ c. $(8.7) + (-9.5)$

d. $-\frac{5}{8} + \frac{1}{2}$

3a. $-3 + 2 + (-5)$ b. $6.0 + (-4.3) + (-1.5)$

4a. $-10 + 7$ b. $-4.5 - 9.1$

5a. $-20 + 7 - 30$ b. $42 - 10 - 3$

An equation is a statement that indicates two expressions are equal. A solution is a number that creates a true statement. To check to see if a number is a solution, plug the given number in for the letter and see if the left side and right side are equal.

Determine whether or not the given number is a solution to the equation by substitution.

6a. $x + 5 = -2$ given $x = -7$ b. $1.8 + z = -3.9$ given $z = 2.1$

c. $|x| + (-7) = -3$ given $x = -4$

d. $x + \left(-\frac{1}{5}\right) = -\frac{1}{4}$ given $x = -\frac{1}{20}$

Quick Quiz

Find the sum.

1. $-32 + 8$

2. $$\begin{array}{r} -108 \\ -105 \\ + \ -98 \\ \hline \end{array}$$

3. $-19.6 + 4.1$

4. $\frac{3}{4} + \left(-\frac{1}{8}\right)$

5. $-\frac{5}{2} + \frac{3}{4}$

6. $9.7 + \left(-12\frac{1}{5}\right)$

Subtraction with Real Numbers

What is the **additive inverse** of a number?

What is an **opposite**?

The sum of a number and its **additive inverse** is ________.

$$a + (-a) = 0$$

Examples

Find the additive inverse of each.

1a. 3 b. −7.3 c. 0

Adding and subtracting real numbers can be approached in two different ways. The first is writing all problems as addition and the second is using the single sign in front of the number to determine the correct step. The answers will be the same.

Using the single sign in front of the numbers to determine the correct step.	
1. Write numbers with a single sign. (Signs same, number + and signs different, number −) 2. Follow rules for addition.	
−3 − (−4)	Read −3 minus −4.
−3 + 4	Signs same, positive value.
1	Signs are different, subtract.
+1	4 is positive and bigger.

Changing all problems to addition.	
When we see subtraction, **add the opposite**. 1. Change subtraction to addition. 2. Change the sign of the following number. 3. Follow rules for addition.	
−3 − (−4)	Read −3 minus −4.
−3 + +4	Add the opposite.
1	The signs are different, subtract.
+1	4 is positive and bigger.

Rules for Addition

The sign(s) in front of the number belong to that number. (Signs same, number + and signs different, number −)
If the signs are the SAME, we find the SUM of the absolute values.
If the signs are DIFFERENT, we find the DIFFERENCE of the absolute values.
Then use the sign of the number with the largest absolute value for the answer.

Examples

Find the following differences.

2a. $(-1) - 4$ b. $(-1) - (-8)$ c. $(10.3) - (-2.3)$

d. $\frac{3}{16}-\left(-\frac{1}{16}\right)$

e. $\left(-\frac{2}{3}\right)-\frac{1}{6}$

3a. $43-(-25)$

b. $-38-(+11)$

c. $-7.3-(-3.2)$

d. $17-(+69)$

To find the change in value between two numbers:
Change in value = (________________) – (________________________)

Examples

4a. At noon on Tuesday the temperature was 34 °F. By noon on Thursday the temperature had changed to −5 °F. How much did the temperature change between Tuesday and Thursday? Write a sentence describing the change in temperature.

b. A jet pilot flew her plane from an altitude of 30,000 ft to an altitude of 12,000 ft. What was the change in altitude? Write a sentence describe the plane's altitude.

5a. Use the table from Example 5 in Learn to determine Susan's **NET SALES**. Write a sentence describing her sale of shoes.

b. Robert weighed 230 lb when he started to diet. The first month he lost 7 lb, the second month he gained 2 lb, and the third month he lost 5 lb. What was his weight after 3 months of dieting? Write a sentence to describe Robert's weight change.

Examples

Determine whether or not the given number is a solution to the equation:

6a. $x-(-6)=-10$ given that $x=-14$

b. $7-y=-1$ given that $y=8$

c. $a-\frac{7}{12}=-\frac{1}{3}$ given that $a=\frac{1}{4}$

Quick Quiz

Find the difference. Reduce if possible.

1. $\begin{array}{r} 27 \\ \underline{-(+42)} \end{array}$

2. $\begin{array}{r} -1.9 \\ \underline{-(-2.6)} \end{array}$

3. $0-(-12)$

4. $-8.5-7.1$

5. $\frac{5}{16}-\frac{9}{16}$

6. $\frac{9}{20}-\left(-\frac{1}{4}\right)$

Multiplication and Division with Real Numbers

Rules for Multiplication of Real Numbers
1. Multiply the two numbers.
2. Determine the sign of each number.
3. Determine the sign of the answer by comparing the two signs. If the signs are the same answer +, if different answer −.

Examples
Multiply. Remember when we multiply fractions, multiply straight across. No need for a common denominator.

1a. $5(-3)$ b. $7(-10)$ c. $42(-1)$

d. $3(-5.2)$ e. $\frac{3}{7} \cdot \left(-\frac{14}{9}\right)$

When multiplying more than two numbers, you can use the properties of multiplication to do some grouping or reordering – be careful to not change the sign of a number when doing so.

Examples

2a. $(-4)(-9)$ b. $-\frac{3}{2}\left(-\frac{2}{9}\right)$

c. $-2(-6.7)$ d. $(-1)(-5)(-3)(-2)$

Zero times anything is equal to ______________.

Examples
3a. $6 \cdot 0$ b. $-13 \cdot 0$

Rules for Division of Real Numbers
1. Divide the two numbers.
2. Determine the sign of each number.
3. Determine the sign of the answer by comparing the two signs. If the signs are the same answer +, if different answer −.

What is 0/any number? What is any number/0? Explain your answers.

Examples

Divide. Remember that dividing by a fraction is to multiply by the reciprocal.

4a. $36 \div 9$ b. $-36 \div 9$ c. $\frac{36}{-9}$

d. $\frac{-36}{-9}$ e. $\frac{8}{0}$ f. $0 \div -6$

5a. $-\frac{16}{7} \div \left(-\frac{2}{21}\right)$ b. $-\frac{20}{12} \div \frac{15}{2}$

Find the quotient to the nearest tenth.

5c. $-5.7 \div 4.2$ d. $-16.54 \div (-5.1)$

Define **Average (Mean)**:

Examples

6a. At noon on five consecutive days in Aspen, Colorado, the temperatures were -5 °F, 7 °F, 6 °F, -7 °F, and 14 °F.
Find the average of these noonday temperatures.

b. In a placement exam for mathematics, a group of ten students had the following scores: 3 students scored 75, 2 students scored 80, 1 student scored 82, 3 students scored 85, and 1 student scored 88.
What was the mean score for this group of students?

Quick Quiz

Find the products. Reduce any fractions to lowest terms.

1. $-11(-2)$
2. $(-6)(-3)(-9)$
3. $-\frac{3}{4} \cdot \left(-\frac{6}{7}\right)$
4. $-27 \cdot 0$

Find the quotients. Reduce any fractions to lowest terms.

5. $(-26) \div (-13)$
6. $-15 \div 0$
7. $-\frac{2}{15} \div \frac{8}{5}$
8. $0 \div -15$

These are written a little differently. Determine the sign for the answer carefully.

9. $-\frac{36}{-9}$
10. $-\frac{4}{0}$
11. $\frac{0}{7}$

Order of Operations with Real Numbers

Rules for Order of Operations: PEMDAS

1.

2.

3.

4.

If there are 6 letters in the pneumonic PEMDAS, why do we list them as four steps for solving problems?

PEMDAS is a mnemonic device that may help you remember the order of operations. Another popular one is "Please Excuse My Dear Aunt Sally's Last Remarks" which stands for Parenthesis, Exponents, Multiply or Divide, Add or Subtract – Left to Right. Perhaps you have made up your own for recalling the steps?

Examples

1a. $36 \div 4 - 6 \cdot 2^2$

b. $2(3^2 - 1) - 3 \cdot 2^3$

c. $-18 \div 6 \cdot 2^2 + (5 - 8)^2 \cdot 2$

d. $9 - 2[(3 \cdot 5 - 7^2) \div 2 + 2^2]$

2. $6(5^2 - 4^2) - 2 \cdot 3^3$

Explain the difference between: -7^2 and $(-7)^2$ and then make a statement on how to handle negative numbers raised to a power. When is the negative repeated in the multiplication and when is it not?

Examples

3a. -3^2 b. $(-3)^2$ c. -6^2 d. $(-6)^2$

When we add or subtract fractions, we need a common denominator.
When we multiply, we multiply across the top (the numerators) and across the bottom (the denominators)
When we divide, we multiply by the reciprocal of the second fraction.

4a. $2\frac{1}{3} \div \left(\frac{1}{4} + \frac{1}{3}\right)$ b. $\frac{3}{5} \cdot \frac{5}{6} + \frac{1}{4} \div \left(\frac{5}{2}\right)^2$

Quick Quiz

Simplify each expression by using the order of operations.

1. $15 \div (-3) \cdot 3 - 10$

2. $-\frac{5}{6} \cdot \frac{3}{4} + \frac{1}{3} \div \frac{1}{2}$

3. $9 - 6[\,(-21) \div 7 \cdot 2 - (-8)\,]$

4. $\left(\frac{1}{2} - 1\frac{3}{4}\right) \div \left(\frac{2}{3} + \frac{3}{4}\right)$

Introduction to Scientific Notation

Define **scientific notation**:

What is scientific notation used for?

List some areas of study or careers that would use scientific notation on a regular basis.

When a number is written in scientific notation,
a positive exponent indicates that the decimal should move to the ________________ .
and a negative exponent indicates that the decimal should move to the _____________.

How do you change a standard number into scientific notation?

Examples

1. Write each of the following in scientific notation.
   a. 8,720,000 b. 0.000000376

2. Change each from scientific notation to standard decimal form.
   a. 9.256×10^7 b. 4.5×10^{-9}

Quick Quiz

Write each power of 10 as an equivalent decimal number.

1. 10^{-7} 2. 10^6

Write each decimal number as an equivalent power of 10.

3. 100,000,000 4. 0.000001

Write each decimal number in scientific notation.

5. 299,800,000 6. 0.000293

Write each number in decimal form.

7. 1.9×10^8 8. 3.25×10^{-6}

Challenge: Given 35.457×10^5, first the 35.457 needs to be adjusted to 3.5457 but now the power needs adjusting. What should the new power be for $3.5457 \times 10^{?}$? Justify or explain your answer. Check yourself by turning both into a standard number.

Properties of Real Numbers

Name of Property	For Addition	For Multiplication
Commutative (The order changes)	$a + b =$ ________	$ab =$ ______
Associative (Grouping changes)	$(a+b)+c =$ ______________	$a(bc)=$ ________
Identity (Identity does not change)	$a + 0 = 0 + a =$ ________ 0 is called the ____________ ____________	$a \cdot 1 = 1 \cdot a =$ _____ 1 is called the ____________ ____________
Inverse	$a + (-a) =$ _____ The additive inverse of a number is its ______________________.	$a \cdot \frac{1}{a} =$ ______ The multiplicative inverse of a number is its ______________.

Zero-Factor Law: $a \cdot 0 = 0 \cdot a$	Example:
Distributive: $a(b + c) = ab + ac$	Example:

Examples

1. State the name of the property being illustrated:
   - a. $(-7) + 13 = 13 + (-7)$ ______________________________
   - b. $8 + (9 + 1) = (8 + 9) + 1$ ______________________________
   - c. $(-25) \cdot 1 = -25$ ______________________________
   - d. $3(x + y) = 3x + 3y$ ______________________________
   - e. $0 \cdot 14 - 0$ ______________________________

	State the name of the property being illustrated	*Substitute the given value to show that the statement is true*
2. a. $x + 14 = 14 + x$ for $\boldsymbol{x} = \mathbf{-4}$		
b. $(3 \cdot 6)x = 3(6x)$ for $\boldsymbol{x} = \mathbf{5}$		
c. $12(y + 3) = 12y + 36$ for $\boldsymbol{y} = \mathbf{-2}$		

Quick Quiz

Complete the expression using the given property. **Do not simplify.**

1. $7 + 3 =$ ________________ commutative property of addition

2. $(6 \cdot 9) \cdot 3 =$ ________________ associative property of multiplication

3. $6\,(5 + 8) =$ ________________ distributive property

4. $5.2 +$ _______ $= 0$ additive inverse property

5. $\frac{1}{5} \cdot$ ______ $= 1$ multiplicative inverse property

6. $8.25 \cdot$ ________ $= 0$ zero-factor law

Simplifying and Evaluating Algebraic Expressions

What is a **variable**?

What is a **coefficient**?

If no number is written in front of a variable, the coefficient is understood to be ________.
Ex. $x = 1x$

If a negative sign $(-)$ is in front of a variable, the coefficient is understood to be ________.
Ex. $-x = -1x$

Like terms (or similar terms) are terms that are constants or terms that contain the same variables raised to the same powers. The coefficients can be different.

Examples

1. From the following list of terms, group the **like terms** together.

$$-7, \quad 2x, \quad 4.1, \quad -x, \quad 3x^2y, \quad 5x, \quad -6x^2y, \quad 0$$

When combining like terms, we add (or subtract) **ONLY** the coefficients to determine the quantity we have of that term.

2. Simplify the expression by combining like terms.

a. $8x + 10x$

b. $6.5y - 2.3y$

c. $2x^2 + 3a + x^2 - a$

d. $4(n - 7) + 5(n + 1)$

e. $\frac{x+3x}{2} + 5x$

When we substitute values into a variable, why is it important to use parentheses around those values?

-6^2	$\neq$	$(-6)^2$
$-(6)(6)$	$\neq$	$(-6)(-6)$
-36	$\neq$	$+36$

Write the procedure to evaluate an algebraic expression:

1.

2.

3.

Examples

3. Evaluate.

a.	x^2
$x = 3$	
$x = -4$	

b.	$-x^2$
$x = 3$	
$x = -4$	

c.	$\frac{(a+b)h}{2}$
$a = 5$ $b = 7$ $h = 3$	

4. Complete the table.

	Combine like terms.	Substitute the given value and evaluate.
a. $2x + 5 + 7x$		$x = -3$
b. $3ab - 4ab + 6a - a$		$a = 2, b = -1$
c. $\frac{5x+3x}{4} + 2(x + 1)$		$x = 5$

Quick Quiz

Simplify each expression by combining like terms.

1. $8x + 10x$

2. $5x + 4 - 8x + 7$

3. $4y + 9x + 12y - 3x$

4. $2.5y - 12 + 3.75 + 2.75y$

Simplify each expression and then evaluate the expression for $a = -4$ and $b = 2.5$.

5. $5a + 20 + 4b + 6b - 12$

6. $-5(a + b) + 2(a - b)$

Solving Linear Equations: $x + b = c$

What is an **equation**?

What is always true about an equation?

If a number is a solution to an equation, what does that mean?

How could you take a possible solution and check to make sure it works?

The goal in solving an equation is to manipulate the terms so that the variable is isolated on one side. In essence, we are undoing the order of operations and thus you might recognize that at times it seems we are "undoing" a problem in the reverse order.

Would it matter if my solution said $x=5$ or $5=x$? Are these the same answer? Getting the lone variable on the left may make things easier for us later when we study inequalities.

The **Addition Principle of Equality** says we can add the same thing to both sides of an equation and it will remain true.

The goal in using this principle is to have a variable isolated, such as $x=$.

Examples

1. Isolate the variable by adding the *opposite of* (-3) to both sides: $x - 3 = 7$

2. Isolate the variable by adding the *opposite of* (5) to both sides: $-11 = y + 5$

Solve the equation. Show your check for each one.

3. $-4.1 + x = 0$

4. $x - \frac{2}{5} = \frac{3}{10}$

5. $3z - 2z + 2 = 3 + 8$

6. $5x - 4x - 1.5 = 6.3 + 4.0$

Step 1 Combine like terms on each side.

Step 2 Solve the equation by isolating the variable.

7. Mark had a coupon for $50 off the Blu-ray player he just purchased. With the coupon, the price was $165.50. Solve the equation $y - 50 = 165.50$ to determine the original price of the Blu-ray player.

Quick Quiz

Solve for the variable.

1. $12 + x = 42$

2. $w - \frac{3}{2} = \frac{5}{2}$

Solving Linear Equations: $ax = c$

The **Multiplication Principle of Equality** says that we can multiply or divide both sides of an equation by the same thing and the equation will remain true.

Steps to Solve Linear Equations in the form $ax=c$.

1.

2.

3.

Examples

1. Solve, show both methods. $5x = 20$

Solve and check each equation.

2. $1.1x + 0.2x = 12.2 - 3.1$

3. $-x = 4$

4. $\frac{4x}{5} = \frac{3}{10}$

Quick Quiz

Solve for the variable.

1. $x - 6 = 1$

2. $32 = 4y$

3. $y + 1.6 = -3.7$

4. $-7.5x = -37.5$

5. $6x - 5x + \frac{3}{4} = -\frac{1}{12}$

6. $1.7x = -5.1 - 1.7$

Solving Percent Problems Using the Equation $R \cdot B = A$

Terms Related to the Basic Equation $R \cdot B = A$

$R =$ ______________________ is a percent in decimal or fraction form
$B =$ ______________________ goes with the word "**of**"
$A =$ ______________________ goes with the word "**is**"

So $R \cdot B = A$ could be translated as "A percent of a number is another number." Often you can read a percent statement and translate it directly to an equation by remembering that

OF	means	"times"
IS	means	"equals"

Examples

Solve by applying the $R \cdot B = A$ equation or by translating to an equation.

1. What is 65% of 800?
2. 42% of what number is 157.5?
3. What percent of 92 is 115?
4. Find 75% of 56.
5. 250 is 62.5% of what number?

Quick Quiz

Use the equation $R \cdot B = A$ or translate to solve for the unknown quantity.

1. 20% of 80 is what number?
2. What percent of 24 is 6?
3. 46 is what percent of 115?
4. Find 175% of 48.

Applications: Discount, Sales Tax, Commission, and Percent Increase/Decrease

Summarize the basic steps for solving application problems.

What are some other strategies you use when solving applications?

Examples

1. A refrigerator that regularly sells for \$1200 is on sale at a 20% discount.
   a. What is the amount of the discount?
   b. What is the sale price?

2. Large fluffy towels were on sale at a discount of 30%. If the sale price was \$8.40, what was the original price?

3. If the sales tax rate is 6%, what would be the final cost of a laptop computer priced at \$899?

4. Susan sells women's shoes. She earns a salary of \$2000 a month plus a commission of 8% on what she sells over \$8500. What did Susan earn the month she sold \$22,500 worth of shoes?

$$\textit{Percent Increase or Decrease} = \frac{\textit{Difference or Change}}{\textit{Original}}$$

Divide to find the decimal, convert to percent.

Examples

5. Ben's last two exam scores in algebra were 80 and 88. What was the percent increase from the first exam to the second?

6. Three years ago you bought a new car for \$25,000. Now you want to trade in your first car. The dealer has told you that the trade in value of your car is now \$17,500. What is the percent decrease in the value of your car?

Quick Quiz

1. People who run a business often have to review quarterly profits for their business to make adjustments to sales plans or item production. The line graph shows the profit per quarter at a small business. Round your answers to the nearest tenth when necessary.

   a. Which quarter had the most profit?

   b. Between which two quarters did sales decrease the most?

   c. What was the percent decrease from part **b.**?

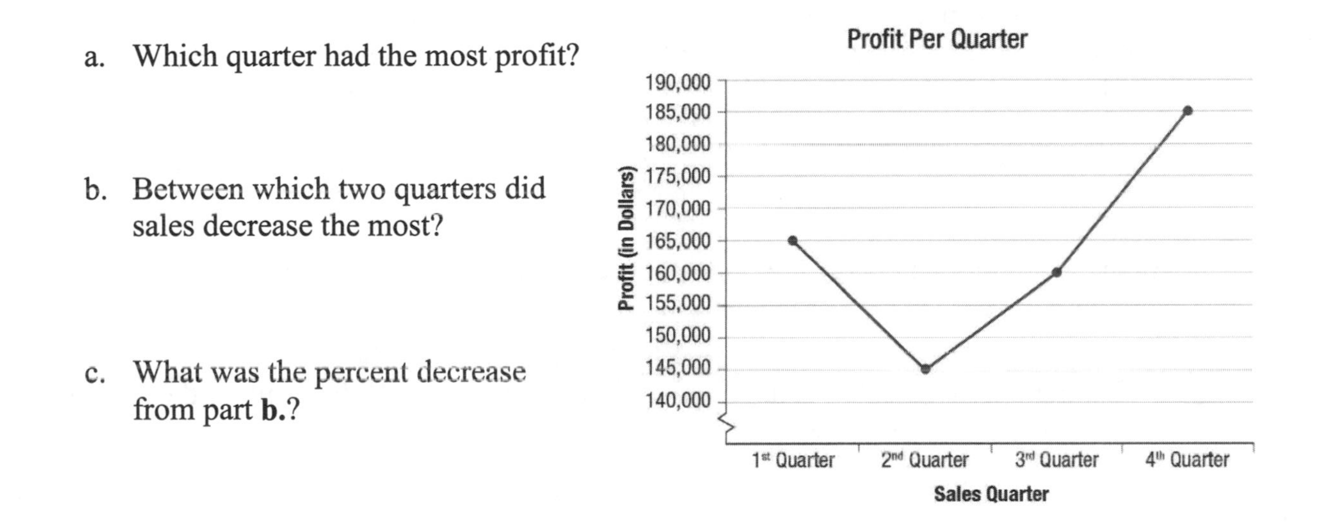

   d. Between which two quarters did sales increase the most?

   e. What was the percent increase from part **d.**?

2. Levi is a full-time sales associate at a computer store. He earns a weekly salary of $220 and earns 15% commission on all of his sales.

   a. During one week, Levi sold $8500 in merchandise. Sales tax in the county where Levi works is 8.5%. What was the total sales tax paid on all of the sales Levi made?

   b. What would Levi's paycheck for the week be before taxes? (**Hint:** Levi's total earnings is equal to salary plus commission.)

   c. Levi's combined federal and state income tax is 23%. How much will his paycheck be after taxes?

   d. During the next week, one of Levi's customers returns $1250 in merchandise. When commission-based purchases are returned, the amount of commission based on the value of the returned merchandise is deducted from the salesperson's next paycheck. How much will be deducted from Levi's next paycheck (before taxes)?

3. At an electronics superstore, a 46-inch flat screen TV has a retail price of $575. Round your answers to the nearest cent when necessary.

   a. During a holiday sale, management decides to offer a 25% discount on the TV. What is the discounted price of the TV?

   b. The superstore also offers a credit card where the customer can save an additional 5% on their entire purchase (after all other discounts and before sales tax) by charging the sale to the store card. If a customer uses the store credit card to buy the discounted TV, what would the final discounted price of the TV be?

   c. The superstore is located in a county with a 6.5% sales tax. What would be the final sales price of the TV for a customer who uses the store credit card?

Applications: Simple Interest

Simple Interest Formula
$I=Prt$

Define each variable from the formula.

$I =$ ________________ $r =$ ________________ a percent in decimal or fraction form

$P =$ ________________ $t =$ ________________ (in years)

Examples

1. You want to borrow \$2000 from your bank for one year. If the interest rate is 5.5%, how much interest would you pay?

2. Sylvia borrowed \$2400 at 5% interest for 90 days (3 months). How much interest did she have to pay? (Keep in mind that 3 months is $\frac{3}{12}$ of a year.)

3. What principal would you need to invest at a rate of 6% to earn \$450 in 6 months? (Keep in mind that 6 months is $\frac{6}{12}$ of a year.)

4. Stuart wants to borrow \$1500 from his father and is willing to pay \$15 in interest. His father told Stuart that he would want interest at 4%. How long can Stuart keep the money?

Quick Quiz

Substitute the given values into the simple interest formula and then simplify to find the interest earned.

1. $P = \$1000$, $r = 5\%$, $t = 3$ years

2. $P = \$2000$, $r = 4\%$, $t = 5$ years

3. $P = \$5000$, $r = 2\%$, $t = 2$ years

4. $P = \$10{,}000$, $r = 6\%$, $t = 4$ months

Perimeter

Define **perimeter**.

There are formulas for perimeter, but if you remember that perimeter is simply the total of all the outer edges, then you don't have to memorize formulas for perimeter.

Examples

1. Find the perimeter of a square with sides of length 16 inches.

2. Find the perimeter of a triangle with sides of lengths 40 mm, 70 mm, and 80 mm.

3. Find the perimeter of a rectangle with length 42 ft and width 26 ft.

A unit that measures on dimension, such as length, is said to be a linear unit. (examples: ft, m, yd). What kind of units are used when we measure perimeter? What are you really measuring when you measure perimeter?

Examples

4. Find the perimeter of a pentagon with sides of lengths 23 cm, 20 cm, 15 cm, 10 cm, and 35 cm.

5. Given a picture of the property…

   a. Find the perimeter of the "L" shaped property. (How many yards of fencing?)

   b. Find the cost of the entire project if the fencing is $12.50 per yard.

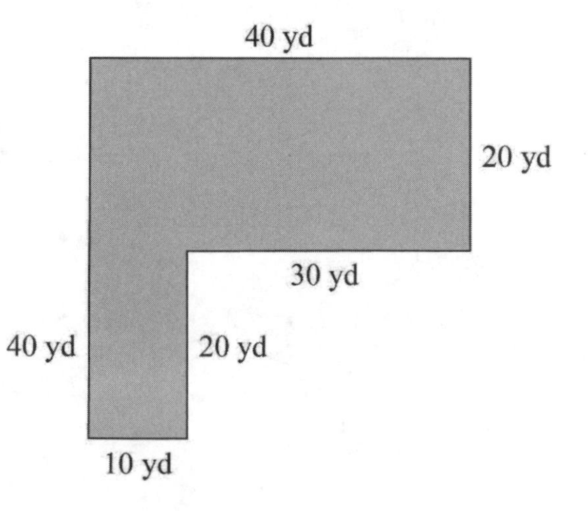

6. If a rectangle has length 15 ft and width 12 ft, what is its perimeter?

   What size rectangle can be cut from one corner so that the perimeter changes? Draw a sketch and explain your answer.

Quick Quiz

Find the perimeter of each figure.

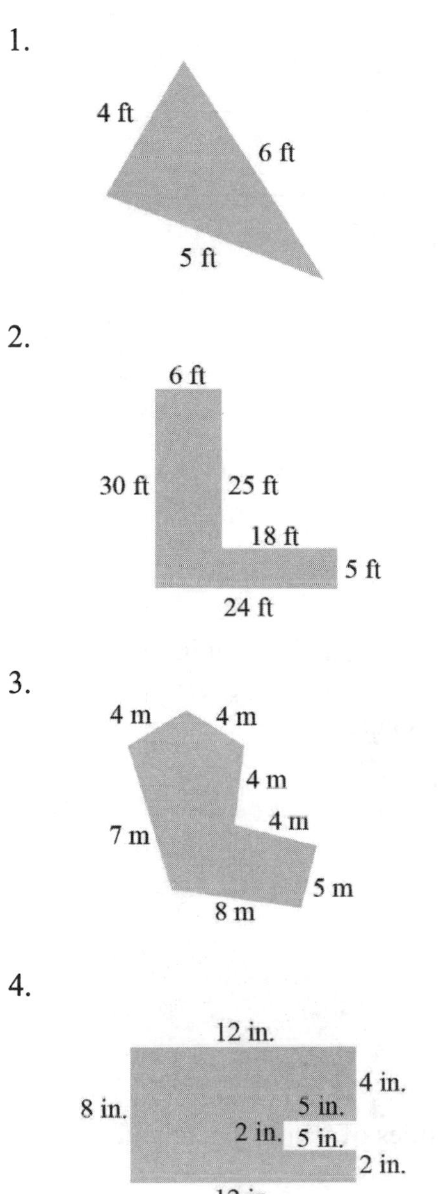

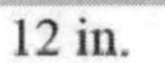

Area

Define **area.**

Why are units for perimeter single units like inches, feet, etc. but units for area are squared like in.^{2}, ft^2, etc.? (Think dimensionally.)

Unlike Perimeter, we need to identify and use formulas to find the area of certain shapes.

Draw a picture of each shape and label the parts, then give its formula for area:

Name	Picture	Formula
Triangle		
Rectangle Square Parallelogram		Which formula works for all 3 shapes?
Trapezoid		

Examples

1. Find the area of a triangle with height 4 in. and base 10 in.

2. Find the area of a trapezoid with altitude 6 in. and parallel sides of length 12 in. and 24 in.

3. Find the area of the figure shown in Learn for example 3. Sketch the figure.

4. A square of 10 ft by 10 ft is removed from a rectangle that is 30 ft by 25 ft. Find the area of what remains in the rectangle.

5. Find the area of the polygon shown. Sketch the figure.

Can you think of a different way to section off this shape? Show how you could find the area using a different method.

6. A baseball infield is in the shape of a square 90 feet on each side.
   a. What is the perimeter of the infield? b. What is the area of the infield?

Quick Quiz

Find the area of each figure.

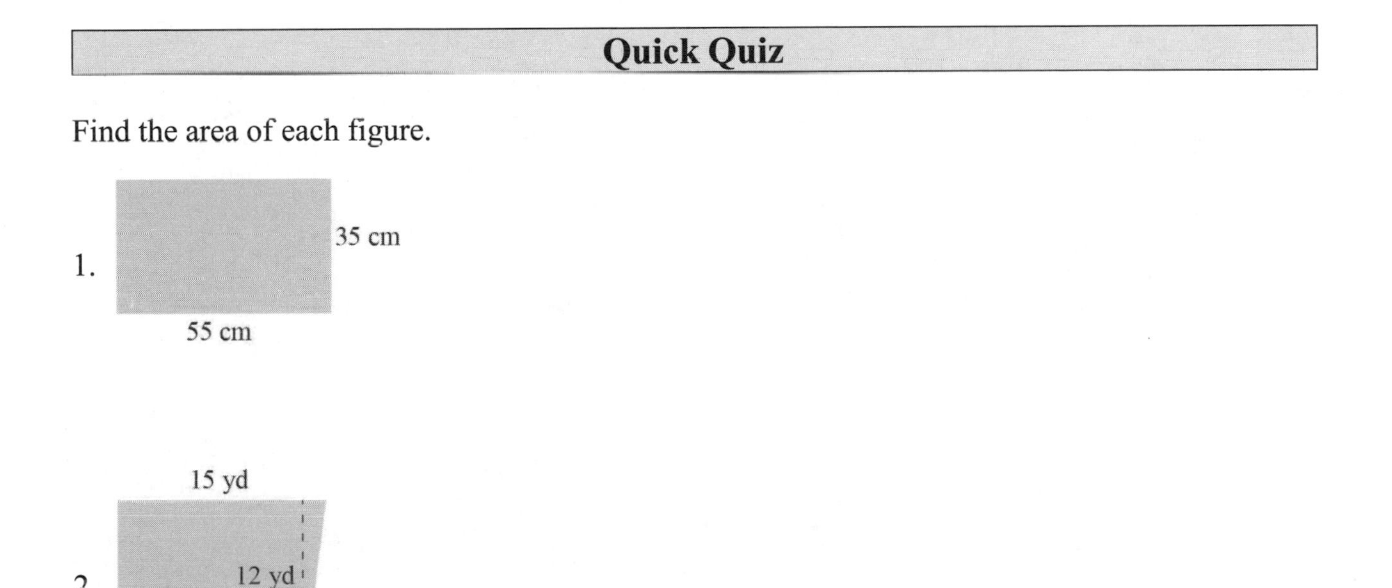

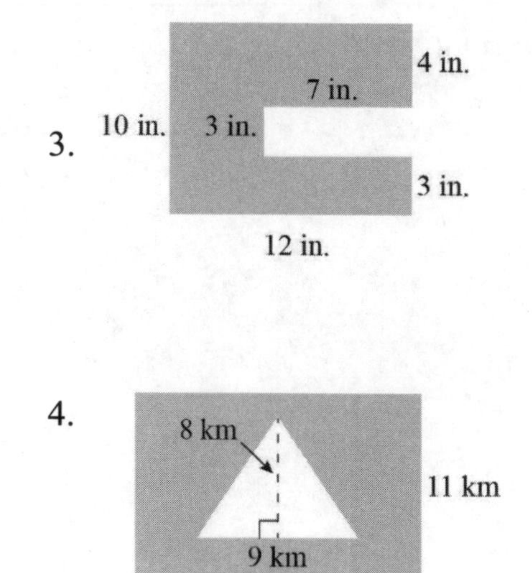
3.
4 in.
7 in.
10 in.
3 in.
3 in.
12 in.
4.
8 km
11 km
9 km
17 km

Circles

Define **radius**.

Define **diameter**.

The perimeter of a circle is called its **circumference**.
And its two formulas are $C=$ and $C=$
What does each variable stand for?

When we want to know how many squares will fit into a circle, we need to find its area.

The formula for the **Area of a Circle** is $A =$ ________ where π is approximately 3.14.

Examples

1. For a circle whose radius is 6 ft
   a. Find its circumference.
   b. Find its area.

2. For a circle with diameter = 5.2 inches
   a. Find its circumference.
   b. Find its area.

3. Find the perimeter of a semicircle with the diameter 20 cm.

4. Find the area of a washer with radius 5 mm and the hole's radius is 2 mm.

5. If we remove a semicircle from the side of a square that is 10 in. by 10 in., what will be the
   a. Perimeter of the remaining part of the square?
   b. Area of the remaining part of the square?

Quick Quiz

Find a. the perimeter and b. the area of each figure. Use $\pi \approx 3.14$ and round to the nearest hundredth.

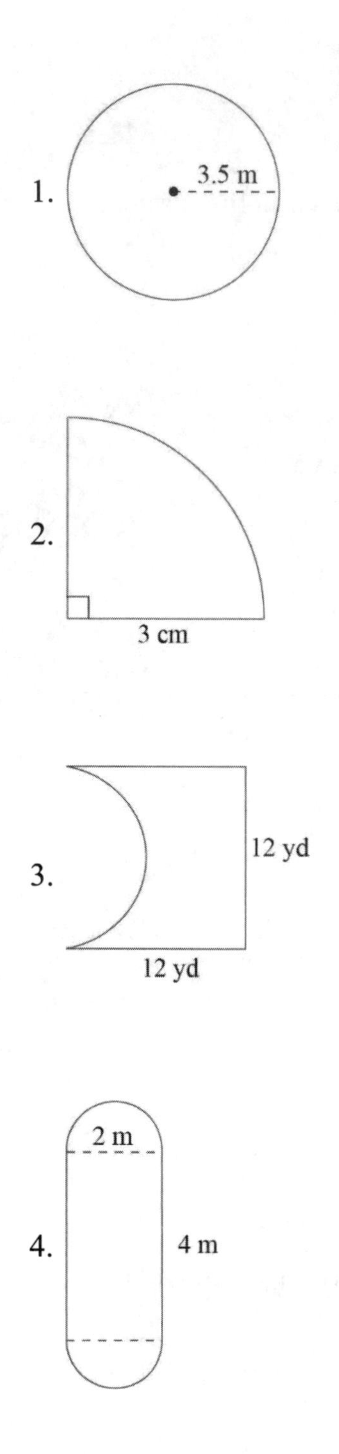

Volume

Define **Volume**.

Why are the units for perimeter single units like inches, the units for area are squared like in.^{2}, and the units for volume cubed like in.^{3}?

When we are finding volume, we are counting how many CUBES will fit inside a three dimensional shape. That is why we use cubic units for measurements of volume. Again, each shape has its own formula for volume and surface area.

Draw and label each shape then give the formula for its volume **(V)**. You will find the formulas for surface area **(SA)** later in this section.

Name	Picture	Formulas
Rectangular solid		V = SA =
Rectangular pyramid		V =
Right circular cylinder		V = SA =
Right circular cone		V =
Sphere		V = SA =

Examples

1. Find the volume of the rectangular solid with length 8 in., width 4 in., and height 1 ft. Write your answer in **cubic inches** and in **cubic feet**.

2. Find the volume of a sphere with radius 9 cm.

3. What is the volume of a cylinder with a height of 10 mm and a circular base with a diameter of 8 mm?

4. Find the volume of the solid pictured in LEARN for example 4. Use the dimensions indicated.

5. Find the volume of a cube with $s = 3$ yd in both cubic yards and cubic feet.

Define **surface area (SA)**.

When we are finding **surface area**, we are counting how many SQUARES will cover the outer surfaces of a three dimensional shape. That is why we use square units for measurements of surface area.

Examples

6. Find the Surface Area of a rectangular solid with dimensions: $l = 30$ cm, $w = 10$ cm, $h = 40$ cm

7. Find the surface area of a cylinder with $r = 2$ in. and $h = 5$ in. Use 3.14 for π.

Since Surface Area is the sum of the areas of all the outer surfaces, can you find the Surface Area for a rectangular pyramid whose base is a square with sides 10 m and whose triangles have heights of 10 m (without a formula)?

Now, go back and fill in the formula for SA on the table.

Quick Quiz

Find the volume of each figure. Use $\pi \approx 3.14$ and round to the nearest hundredth.

1. 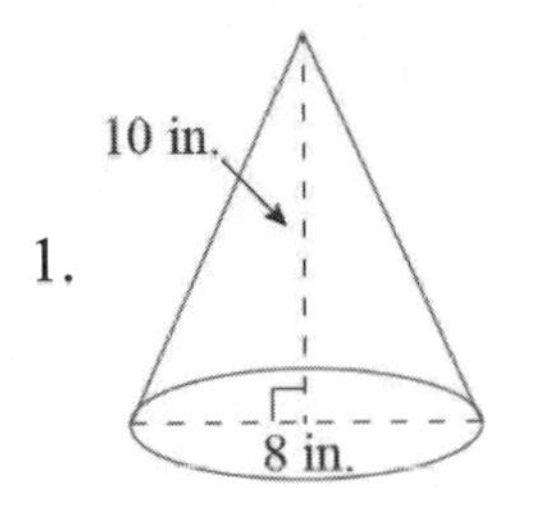

2. 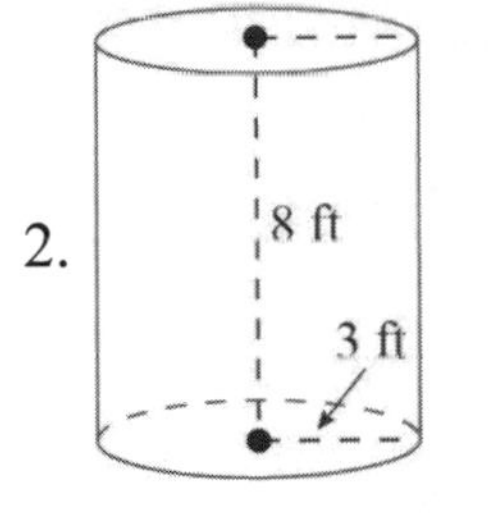

3. 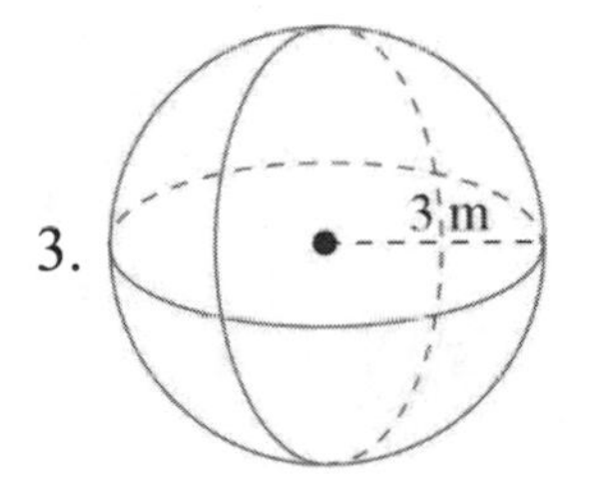

4. 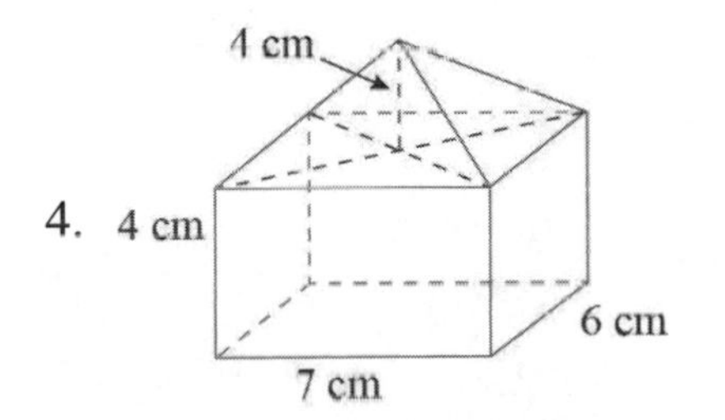

Vocabulary Check

Define each of the following terms in your own words, providing examples as necessary to clarify the term.

Area

Circumference

Diameter

Equation

Exponents

Expression

Integers

Irrational numbers

Like terms

Mean

Natural numbers

Order of operations

Perimeter

Pi

Radius

Rational numbers

Scientific Notation

Simple Interest formula

Square root

Surface Area

Volume

Whole numbers

Concept Review

Answer the following questions as completely as possible in your own words. Make sure to get the big points of each with key steps involved.

1. How do you determine the absolute value of a number?

2. How do you add or subtract signed numbers?

3. How do you multiply or divide signed numbers?

4. How do we classify numbers? (real, rational, etc.)

5. How do you know when to add vs. subtract real numbers? How do you determine the sign of the answer?

6. What are the rules for multiplying and dividing real numbers?

7. What is the difference between $(-3)^4$ and -3^4?

8. How do you evaluate powers of numbers?

9. What is the order of operations and how do you apply it?

10. When following order of operations, what is important to remember about the sign in front of a number?

11. What is the difference between an expression and an equation?

12. What does it mean to find a solution to an equation?

13. How do you check to see if your solution is correct?

14. When a variable does not have a number in front of it what can be put there?

15. How do you combine like terms?

16. What do the following properties allow us to do?
    a. Commutative Property
    b. Associative Property
    c. Inverse Property
    d. Distributive Property
    e. Identity Property

17. What do the following words mean?
    a. Term
    b. Variable
    c. Coefficient
    d. Constant

18. What does it mean to evaluate an expression and how do you do it?

19. How do you simplify an expression?

20. What does distribute mean?

21. What are the steps for solving an equation?

22. How do you eliminate fractions in an equation?

23. How do you check an equation?

24. When a variable does not have a number in front of it what can be put there?

25. How do you calculate a basic percent problem?

26. What are powers of 10?

27. How do you convert between standard notation and scientific notation?

28. How do you convert between scientific notation and standard notation?

29. How do you solve application problems involving

    a. area

    b. perimeter

    c. volume

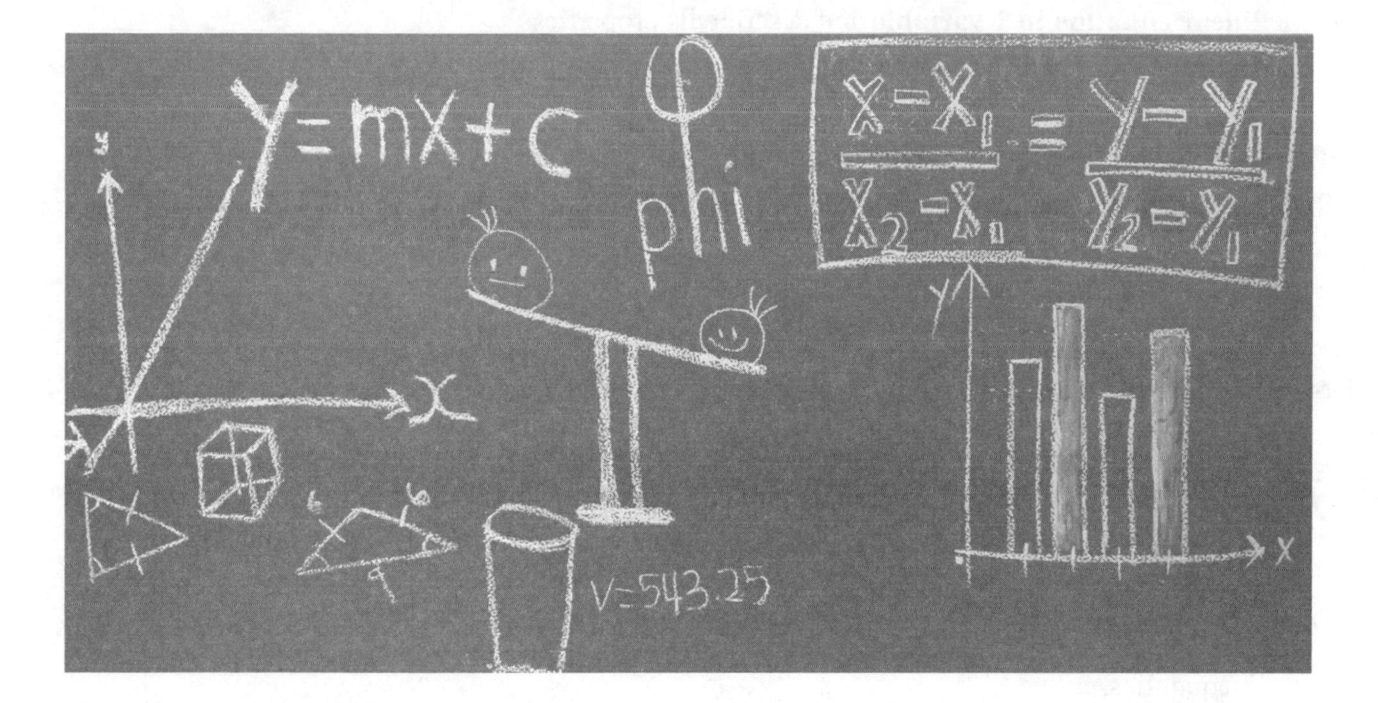

Unit 4
First Degree Equations and Inequalities in One Variable

Solving Linear Equations: $x + b = c$

Define **linear equation in 1 variable** and describe its properties.

Remember: $x^1 = x$ and $x = x^1$

What is always true about an equation?

If a number is a solution to an equation, what does that mean?

How could you take a possible solution and check to make sure it works?

The goal in solving an equation is to manipulate the terms so that the variable is isolated on one side. In essence, we are undoing the order of operations and thus you might recognize that at times it seems we are "undoing" a problem in the reverse order.

Would it matter if my solution said $x = 5$ or $5 = x$? Are these the same answer? Getting the lone variable on the left may make things easier for us later when we study inequalities.

The **Addition Principle of Equality** says we can add the same thing to both sides of an equation and it will remain true.

Steps to Solve a Linear Equation of the form $x + b = c$:

1.

2.

3.

How many solutions does a linear equation have?

There are times when an equation has no solution – no number when plugged in will make both sides equal. Other times, an equation could have infinite solutions like $x = x$ because both sides are equal all the time. But all other times a linear equation of one variable will have exactly one answer, never exactly 2 or exactly 3.

Examples

Solve and check. Remember adding and subtracting fractions requires a common denominator.

1. $x - 3 = 7$ 2. $-11 = y + 5$ 3. $-4.1 + x = 0$

4. $x - \frac{2}{5} = \frac{3}{10}$ 5. $3z - 2z + 2 = 3 + 8$

6. $5x - 4x - 1.5 = 6.3 + 4.0$

7. Mark had a coupon for $50 off the Blu-Ray player he just purchased. With the coupon, the price was $165.50. Solve the equation $y - 50 = 165.50$ to determine the original price of the Blu-Ray player.

Quick Quiz

Solve and check.

1. $x - 6 = 1$ 2. $y + 1.6 = -3.7$ 3. $6x - 5x + \frac{3}{4} = -\frac{1}{12}$

Solving Linear Equations: $ax = c$

What is a **reciprocal**? What is the reciprocal of $\frac{3}{4}$? _____

Remember that dividing by a constant is the same as multiplying by its reciprocal.

The **Multiplication Principle of Equality** says that we can multiply or divide both sides of an equation by the same thing and the equation will remain true.

Steps to Solve a Linear Equation of the form $ax = c$

1.

2.

3.

Examples

Solve and check. Remember dividing by a fraction is the same as multiplying by its reciprocal.

1. $5x = 20$

2. $1.1x + 0.2x = 12.2 - 3.1$

Since the number in front of a variable is called the coefficient, what is the **coefficient** of $-x$?

3. $-x = 4$

4. $\frac{4x}{5} = \frac{3}{10}$

Quick Quiz

Solve and check.

1. $32 = 4y$

2. $-7.5x = -37.5$

3. $1.7x = -5.1 - 1.7$

Solving Linear Equations: $ax + b = c$

We are getting ready to combine the two types of equations we just learned how to solve. Now we will need to apply both properties of addition and multiplication.

Steps to Solve a Linear Equations of the form $ax + b = c$

1.

2.

3.

4.

Examples

Solve and check.

1. $3x + 3 = -18$

2. $9x - 12 - 5x = 0$

3. $-26 = 2y - 2(7 + 2y)$

4. $16.53 - 18.2z = 7.43$

If your equation includes fractions, how can you apply the multiplication property of equality to clear the fractions from the entire equation? List all steps.

Examples

5. $5.1x + 7.4 - 1.8x = -9.1$

6. $\frac{5}{6}x - \frac{5}{2} = -\frac{10}{9}$

What if one of the terms is not a fraction? Does it get the same treatment as above? How can you make it look like a fraction?

7. $\frac{1}{2}x + \frac{3}{4}x + \frac{5}{2} - \frac{2}{3}x = -1$

8. $\frac{3}{4}y + \frac{1}{2} = \frac{5}{8}$

When would you consider it especially important to "check" your answer by substituting the solution into the original equation? Can you sometimes do a mental check?

Quick Quiz

Solve and check each linear equation.

1. $3x + 11 = 2$

2. $14 + 9t = 5$

3. $0.2n - 1.2 + 0.1n = 0$

4. $\frac{1}{2} - \frac{3}{8}x = \frac{5}{6}$

5. $4.7 - 0.5x - 0.3x = -0.1$

6. $\frac{5}{8}x - \frac{1}{4}x + \frac{1}{2} = \frac{3}{10}$

Solving Linear Equations: $ax + b = cx + d$

What is a **variable**?

What is a **constant**?

Summary of steps for **Solving Linear Equations**

1. Clear the equation of fractions by multiplying all terms by a common denominator.
2. Simplify each side of the equation by distributing and combining like terms.
3. Move all variable terms to one side by adding the opposite to both sides.
4. Move all constants to the other side by adding the opposite to both sides.
5. Force the variable to have a coefficient of 1 ($1x$ vs. $4x$) by multiplying by the coefficient of the variable. (or multiplying by its reciprocal)
6. Reduce any fraction answers.
7. State your answer.
8. Substitute in your answers to the original to check if both sides are equal.

How do **you** decide whether to put your variables on the right or the left?

Examples

Solve.

1. $5x + 3 = 2x - 18$

2. $4x + 1 - x = 2x - 13 + 5$

3. $6y + 2.5 = 7y - 3.6$

4. $\frac{1}{3}x + \frac{13}{15} = \frac{3}{5}x - 1$

5. $2(y - 7) = 4(y + 1) - 26$

6. $-2(5x + 13) - 2 = -6(3x - 2) - 41$

7. $4(x + 3) = 2(3x - 1) + 6$

8. $3(x+5)+1 = -11$

9. $3(x-25)+3x = 6(x+10)$

10. $-2(x-7)+x = 14-x$

How many solutions does each equation have for examples 8, 9, and 10? When the variable was eliminated completely, what does that tell us about the solution to the equation?

Define **contradiction**.

Define **identity**.

Which of the solutions above would be labeled using these terms?

If you think the solution is a contradiction (no solution) or identity (infinite solutions), how can you check that equation to see if your solution is correct?

Quick Quiz

Solve and check each linear equation.

1. $4n-3 = n+6$

2. $2(x+1) = 3x+3$

3. $\frac{y}{5}+\frac{3}{4}=\frac{y}{2}+\frac{3}{4}$

4. $0.4(x+3) = 0.3(x-6)$

Working with Formulas

The first steps in successfully working with formulas are to identify the correct formula and define the meaning of each variable being used.

Describe what each formula is describing and the meaning of each variable.

Formula (Description or Use)	Meaning
$I = Prt$	I: P: t:
$C = \frac{5}{9}(F - 32)$	C: F:
$d = rt$	d: r: t:
$P = 2l + 2w$	P: l: w:
$P = a + b + c$	P: a, b, c:

The capitalization of a variable is important. The variables P and p do not represent the same values.

Examples

Solve by applying the appropriate formula. State your answer in a sentence.

1. Maribel loaned $5,000 to a friend for 90 days at an annual interest rate of 8%. How much will her friend pay her at the end of 90 days?

2. What is 212°F in Celsius? What is 20°C in Fahrenheit?

3. The lifting force F exerted on an airplane wing is found by multiplying some constant k by the area A of the wing's surface and by the square of the plane's velocity v. The formula is $F = kAv^2$. Find the force on a plane's wing during takeoff if the area of the wing is 120ft^2, k is $\frac{4}{3}$, and the plane is traveling 80 miles per hour during takeoff.

When given a formula and values for some of the variables, how do you find the value of the missing variable?

4. The perimeter of a triangle is 38 feet. One side is 5 feet long and a second side is 18 feet long. How long is the third side?

When solving an equation for a given variable, all other variables should be treated as what? How do you solve for that given variable?

5. Given: $d = rt$ we say that d is solved "in terms of" r and t.
Solve this formula for t in terms of d and r.

6. Given: $V = \frac{k}{P}$ we say that V is solved in terms of what?
Solve this equation for P in terms of V and k.

7. Given: $C = \frac{5}{9}(F - 32)$ Solve for F in terms of C.

8. Given: $2x + 4y = 10$
Solve for x in terms of y.
Solve for y in terms of x.

9. Solve for y in terms of x.
$3x - y = 15$

List a job or career where you would need to use a formula.

Quick Quiz

Evaluate each formula for the given values. Use $\pi = 3.14$ when needed.

1. $F = Ma$; $M = 250$ kg; $a = 9.8$ m/s^2

2. $L = 2\pi rh$; $r = 15$ cm; $h = 20$ cm

Solve each equation for the indicated variable.

3. $I = Prt$ Solve for t.

4. $V = \frac{1}{3}bh$ Solve for h.

Translating English Phrases and Algebraic Expressions

Complete the table by adding words that can translate into the underlined words below.

Addition (Sum)	**Subtraction** (Difference)	**Multiplication** (Product)	**Division** (Quotient)	**Exponents**
	Subtracted from			
More than	Less than			

The words "than" and "from" indicate the expression should be written in reverse. So 7 subtracted from 12 is 12 − 7. Highlight the ones above that indicate a need to reverse the numbers. The words in ( ) above indicate that the parentheses are needed in addition to the +, −, ×, ÷ creating some grouping of numbers.

When translating expressions, translate left to right as you read except when you encounter the words "than" or "from." Make sure to pay close attention to words that indicate parentheses are needed.

Examples

1. Write an English phrase for each algebraic expression. Work to use different words.

a.	$3x$	
b.	$z + 3$	
c.	$2(x + 1)$	
d.	$2x + 1$	
e.	$5n - 3$	
f.	x^2	
g.	n^3	

2. Write an algebraic expression for each phrase.

a.		The product of five and a number
b.		Twice a number increased by eight
c.		Three times the difference between a number and two

3. Translate each algebraic expression into an English phrase.

a.	$\frac{x}{-4}$	
b.	$5y - 6$	
c.	$2(3 + n)$	
d.	$60h$	
e.	$30 + 0.25x$	

Why can the phrase, "a number added to 5" be written as $5 + n$ AND $n + 5$ without changing the outcome? Why does the phrase "a number subtracted from 5" HAVE to be written as $5 - n$ and cannot be written as $n - 5$? Give some examples to illustrate the problem.

Quick Quiz

Translate each English phrase into an algebraic expression.

1. four less than a number

2. five more than three times a number

3. the quotient of seven and the difference between three and a number

4. the sum of a number and six times the number

5. six less than a number

6. six less a number

7. four less than twice a number

8. four less twice a number

Applications: Number Problems and Consecutive Integers

Translating creates equations that can then be solved to find missing values. When translating expressions, translate left to right as you read except when you encounter the words "than" or "from." Sometimes additional information is needed to relate two variables. Make sure to pay close attention to words that indicate parentheses are needed.

While some applications cannot be translated directly into an equation, the same key words used in translating will indicate how the concepts in the problem are related to create an equation.

What are words that mean equal?

Examples

Translate each into an equation, solve the equation, and check the solution.

1. If a number is decreased by 36, and the result is 76 less than twice the number, what is the number?

2. Three times the sum of a number and 5 is equal to twice the number plus 5. Find the number.

3. One integer is 4 more than 3 times a second integer. Their sum is 24. What are the two integers?

What is an **integer**? Remember: integer is pronounced with the "j" sound.

Describe the algebraic relationship between the following integer relationships.

Consecutive Integers	Consecutive Even Integers	Consecutive Odd Integers

Why do we use even numbers to represent odd numbers? In other words, why are n, $n+2$, $n+4$, etc. used to represent both consecutive even and consecutive odd integers?

Examples

Translate each into an equation, solve the equation, and check the solution.

4. The sum of three consecutive odd integers is -3. What are the integers?

5. Find three consecutive integers such that the sum of the first and third is 76 less than three times the second. Then check.

6. Joe wants to budget $\frac{2}{5}$ of his monthly income for rent. He found an apartment he likes for $800 a month. What monthly income does he need to be able to afford this apartment?

7. A student bought a calculator and a textbook for a total of $200.80 (including tax). The textbook cost $20.50 more than the calculator. He then challenged a friend to calculate the cost of each item.

Quick Quiz

Solve and check.

1. Five less than a number is equal to thirteen decreased by the number. Find the number.

2. Two added to the quotient of a number and seven is equal to negative three. What is the number?

3. The sum of three consecutive even integers is 78. What are the integers?

4. Find three consecutive integers whose sum is one hundred sixty-eight more than the second number.

Applications: Distance-Rate-Time, Interest, Average

What is the distance formula?

Is distance ever negative?

What does each variable represent?

What are the units for each variable?

If you wanted to have a formula for $t =$, how could you algebraically change $D = rt$ to represent a formula for time?

Examples

Solve each application showing your method and work. Check your solution for reasonableness.

1. A brother and sister leave a family reunion at the same time and drive their cars in opposite directions. The brother's speed is 50 mph and the sister's speed is 65 mph. When will they be 460 miles apart?

2. A motorist averaged 45 mph for the first part of a trip and 54 mph for the last part of the trip. If the total trip of 303 miles took 6 hours, what was the time for each part?

What is the interest formula?

What does interest mean?

What does each variable represent?

What are the units for each variable?

If you wanted to know how much money you had in your savings account total after computing the interest earned, how could you find that? Which should be more, the interest earned or the total in savings?

Examples

Solve each application showing your method and work. Check your solution for reasonableness.

3. Kara has had $40,000 invested for one year, some in a savings account which paid 7% and the rest in a high-risk stock which yielded 12% for the year. If her interest income last year was $3550, how much did she have in the savings account and how much did she invest in the stock?

How do you find the average (or mean) of a set of numbers?

Examples

Solve each application showing your method and work. Check your solution for reasonableness.

4. Suppose you have scores of 85, 92, 82, and 88 on four exams in your class. What score will you need on a fifth exam to have an average of 90?

5. A jeweler paid $350 for a ring. He wants to price the ring for sale so that he can give a 30% discount on the marked selling price and still make a profit of 20% on his cost. What should be the marked selling price of the ring?

Quick Quiz

Solve each application showing your method and work. Check your solution for reasonableness.

1. Achilles is racing a tortoise and gives him a 2-hour head start. The tortoise runs at a pace of 10 miles per hour and Achilles runs at a pace of 25 miles per hour.

   How long will it take Achilles to catch up to the tortoise?

   If the race is 35 miles long, will Achilles pass the tortoise before crossing the finish line?

2. Savannah invests $3600 per year into her retirement account, a portion of which is a contribution match from her employer. Savannah invests the employer match in a high-risk fund that averages return of 8% and invests the rest in a low-risk account that averages a return of 4%. She wants to earn a total of $198 in interest for the year. How much should be invested in each fund?

3. Kevin consulted a dietician who told him to consume an average of 2100 calories per day based on his age, current weight, activity level, and weight goals. Kevin consumed 2050 calories on Monday, 2200 on Tuesday, 2300 on Wednesday, and 2400 on Thursday. How many would he need to consume on Friday to average 2100 calories per day for the five days? Active men should consume more than 1500 calories/day to avoid triggering "starvation mode" in the body. As a dietician what conversation would you have with Kevin?

Solving Absolute Value Equations

Solving Absolute Value Equations

Step 1: Isolate the absolute value.

Step 2: Rewrite the equation without the absolute value bars recognizing that the value of what is inside the bars can be positive or negative.

If $|AV|$ = positive, then we have 2 solutions: AV = pos and AV = neg

If $|AV|$ = zero , then we have 1 solution: AV = 0

If $|AV|$ = negative, then we have no solution Ø because absolute values can't be negative.

Step 3: Check all possible solutions by substituting them back into the original equation.

Examples

Solve each equation.

1a. $|x| = 5$

b. $|3x - 4| = 5$

c. $|4x - 1| = -8$

d. $5|3x + 17| - 4 = 51$

Quick Quiz

Solve and check each equation.

1. $|t| = 5$

2. $|2x - 4| = 8$

3. $3|2x + 1| - 6 = 12$

4. $-2|x + 7| = 8$

Linear Inequalities

Set-Builder Notation is a formal way of describing a list of numbers and uses mathematical symbols to indicate words.

{ } means the "set of" x represents the numbers | means "such that"

What is placed after the bar gives the condition for that set of numbers.

For example: $\{x \mid x > 5\}$ reads "the set of numbers, x, such that x is greater than 5."

What is a **union** between two sets?

What symbol is used? What word can replace that symbol?

What is the **intersection** between two sets?

What symbol is used? What word can replace that symbol?

How can $7 < x$ be rewritten so it can more easily be read as "x is…"?
The variable is always read first regardless of order written.

How do you read $-3 < x < 6$?
How can it be rewritten using the word "and"?

Interval notation is a method we use to communicate the solution graphed on a number line without the need for the graph. Its use makes written communication using technology easier.

Symbols: The chart below compares the different inequality symbols with the interval notation symbols. Interval notation uses the same symbol on both graph and in solutions versus using the inequality and graphing symbol.

Inequality	Common Graphing Symbol	Interval Notation
$<$ or $>$	○ open	Use (or)
$\leq$ or $\geq$	● closed	Use [or] Hint: Notice how the top and bottom of a bracket make an = sign.
When working with ∞ or $-\infty$, use the (or) because it is understood that we can never quite reach the point of infinity.		
Describe the graph always from left to right: [***left hand end***, ***right hand end***) Whether you use [or) depends on the inequality symbol. The symbol ∩ or ∪ is used when a graph has multiple parts.		

What is an **open interval**? What is a **closed interval**? What is a **half-open interval**?

Examples

Graph each inequality and describe the graph using interval notation.

1. $x > 3$

2. $0 < x \leq 4$

3. $[1, \infty)$

4. $-3 < x < 1$

The "Union" of two sets is based on the concept of "**or**" and implies that only one of the given conditions needs to be satisfied.
What does the "Intersection" of two sets, "**and**", imply in regards to meeting the given conditions?

Examples

Graph the set and describe the graph using interval notation.

5. $\{x|x > 5 \text{ or } x \leq 4\}$

6. $\{x|x \leq 2 \text{ and } x \geq 0\}$ This set can also be written as $\{x|$ ___ $\leq x \leq$ ___$\}$

What is the difference between a **linear equation** and a **linear inequality**?

Solving a linear inequality is exactly the same as solving an equation except if you multiply or divide by a negative number. What needs to happen when you multiply or divide both sides by a negative number at any time during the process?

Examples

Solve, graph, and state your solution using interval notation. Check your solution.

7. $6x + 5 \leq -1$

8. $x - 3 > 3x + 4$

9. $6 - 4x \leq x + 1$

10. $2x + 5 < 3x - (7 - x)$

Solve as a compound inequality or rewrite as an intersection. Graph and give the solution in interval notation.

11. $-5 \leq 4x - 1 < 11$

12. $5 \leq -3 - 2x \leq 13$

13. $0 < \frac{3x-5}{4} < 3$

14. A math student has grades of 85, 98, 93, and 90 on four examinations. If he must average 90 or better to receive an A for the course, what scores can he receive on the final exam and earn an A?

15. Ellen is going to buy 30 stamps, some 28-cent and some 44-cent. If she has $9.68, what is the maximum number of 44-cent stamps she can buy?

When solving a linear inequality, under what conditions could the solution include all real numbers? How would you recognize it? What would the graph look like? And when might the solution be no solution? How would you recognize that?

Quick Quiz

Solve, graph, and state your solution using interval notation. Check your solution.

1. $2x + 3 < 5$

2. $\frac{x}{3} - x > 1 - \frac{x}{3}$

3. $0.9x - 11.3 \leq 3.1 - 0.7x$

4. $\frac{2(x-1)}{3} < \frac{3(x+1)}{4}$

5. $2 \leq -x + 2 \leq 6$

6. $0.9x < 3x + 2.4 < 6.9$

Vocabulary Check

Define each of the following terms in your own words, providing examples as necessary to clarify the term.

Absolute Value

Algebraic Notation

Average

Coefficient

$D = rt$

Even Integers

$I = Prt$

Integers

Interval Notation

Like Terms

Linear Equation

Linear Inequality

Odd Integers

Concept Review

Answer the following questions as completely as possible in your own words. Make sure to get the big points of each with key steps involved.

1. What is an equation?
2. How do you determine if you have a linear equation in one variable?
3. What does it mean to solve an equation?
4. How do you determine if a given value is a solution to an equation?

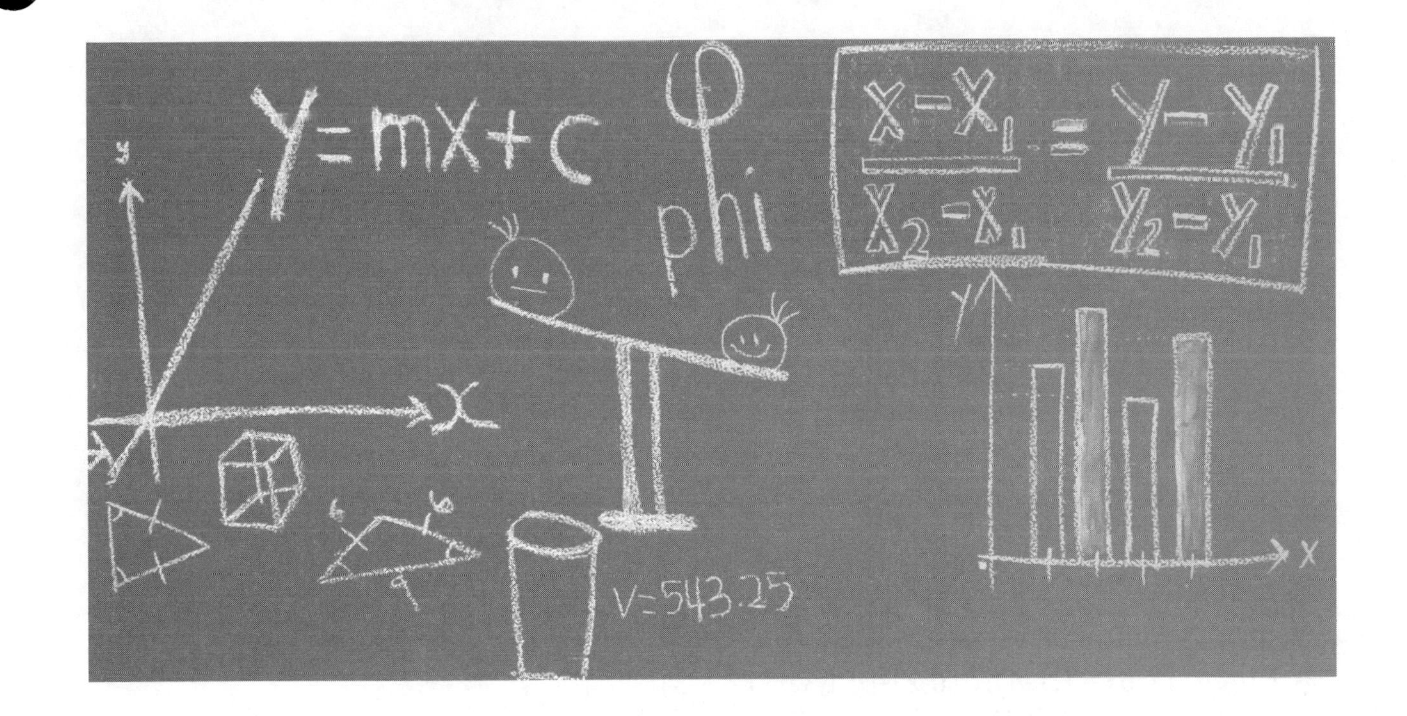

Unit 5

Linear Equations, Inequalities, and Systems of Linear Equations in Two Variables

The Cartesian Coordinate System

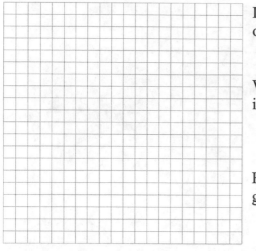

Draw and label each **axis**, each **quadrant**, and the **origin** on the graph to the left.

What does an **ordered pair** look like and what information does it give?

How do you plot a point on a coordinate plane when given its ordered pair?

Examples

Draw both axes. Plot and label the ordered pairs.

1a. $\{A(-2,1), B(-1,-4), C(0,2), D(1,3), E(2,-3)\}$

b. $\{A(-1,3), B(0,1), C(1,-1), D(2,-3), E(3,-5)\}$

1a. 1b.

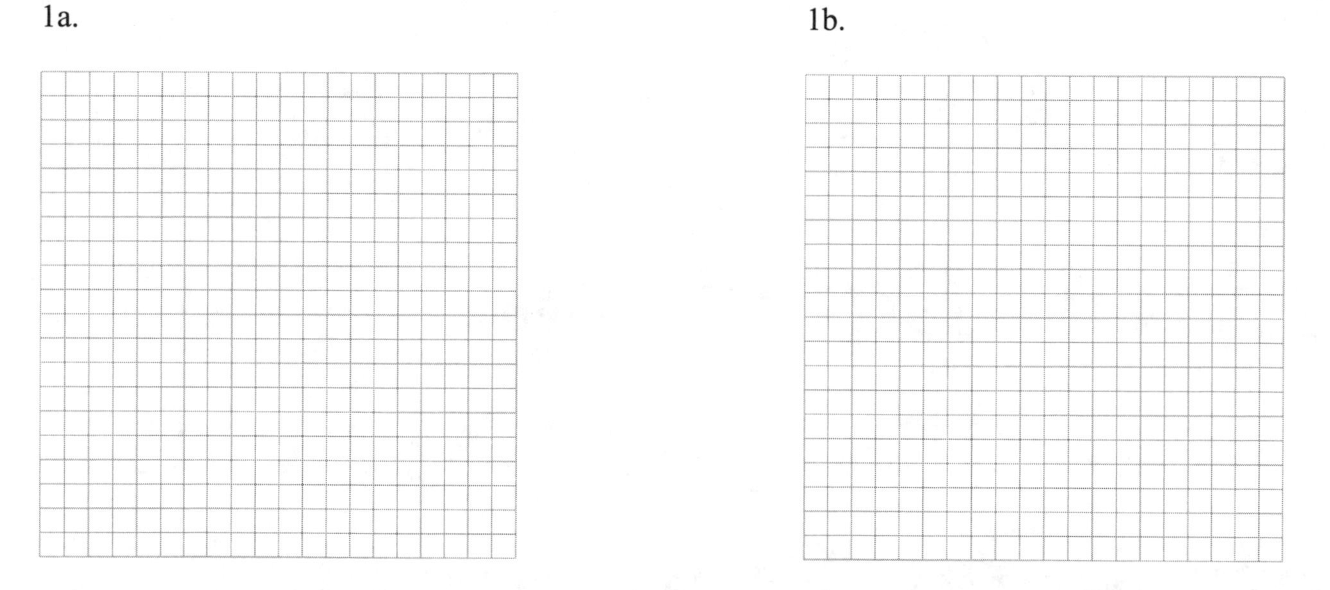

When two points are connected, the result is a line. Lines go on infinitely in both directions. Therefore, ANY number chosen for x will always have a matching value for y. The values being used for "x" are arbitrary and other values can be used in place of them and the same line will result.

Consider the equation: $y = 2x + 3$ complete the ordered pairs below.

x	y
1	
-2	
$\frac{1}{2}$	

What if instead of picking a value for x, the value 5 was picked for y?
Why did the result give us the same pair of numbers that resulted when $x = 1$?

Which coordinate of an ordered pair is the independent variable?

Which one is the dependent variable?

How do we determine if an ordered pair is a solution to an equation?

Examples

2a. Determine which of the ordered pairs $(0, -2), (\frac{2}{3}, 0), (2,5)$ satisfy the equation $y = 3x - 2$.

$(0, -2)$ $(\frac{2}{3}, 0)$ $(2, 5)$

b. Determine the missing coordinates that satisfy $2x + 3y = 12$.

$(0,\quad)$ $(3,\quad)$ $(\quad, 0)$ $(\quad, -2)$

c. Complete the table for $y = 1 - 2x$.

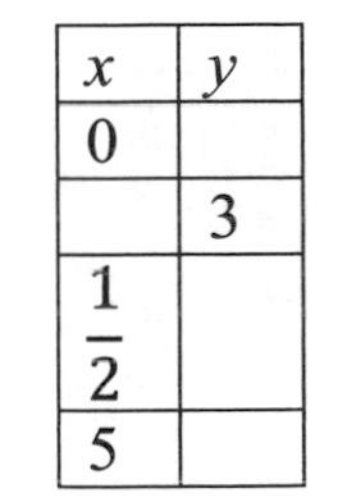

x	y
0	
	3
$\frac{1}{2}$	
5	

Use the given graphs to identify three points on each line.

3a. b.

What does it mean to be a point on the line?
What does it mean to be a solution to an equation?

Quick Quiz

Complete the tables of ordered pairs for each equation.

1.

$y = 3x$	
x	y
0	
	−3
−2	
	6

2.

$\frac{1}{2}x - \frac{1}{4}y = 12$	
x	y
0	
	0
10	
	8

3. Choose a value for x and solve for y to create ordered pairs.

$y = \frac{1}{3}x + 6$	
x	y

Graphing Linear Equations in Two Variables

An equation written in this form $Ax + By = C$ is said to be in ________________ form.

Write $3 - 3x = y$ in standard form:

A unique line is determined by how many points?

What might we accomplish by finding a third point?

Describe the steps to graph a line.

Examples

Complete the table and graph each of the following linear equations. Pick two extra values for additional points.

1a. $2x+3y=6$

x	y
0	
-3	
	0
	$\frac{1}{3}$

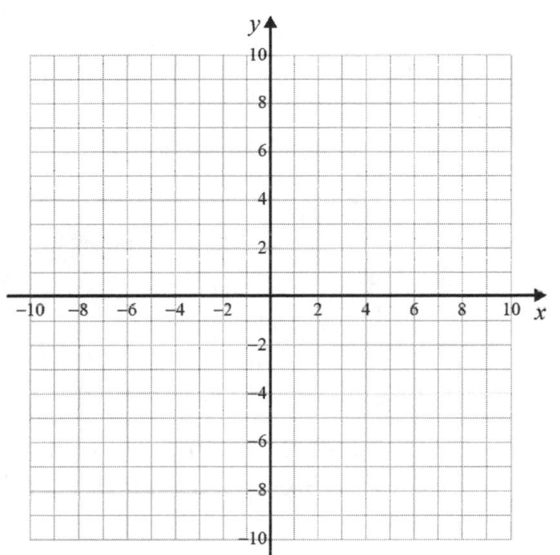

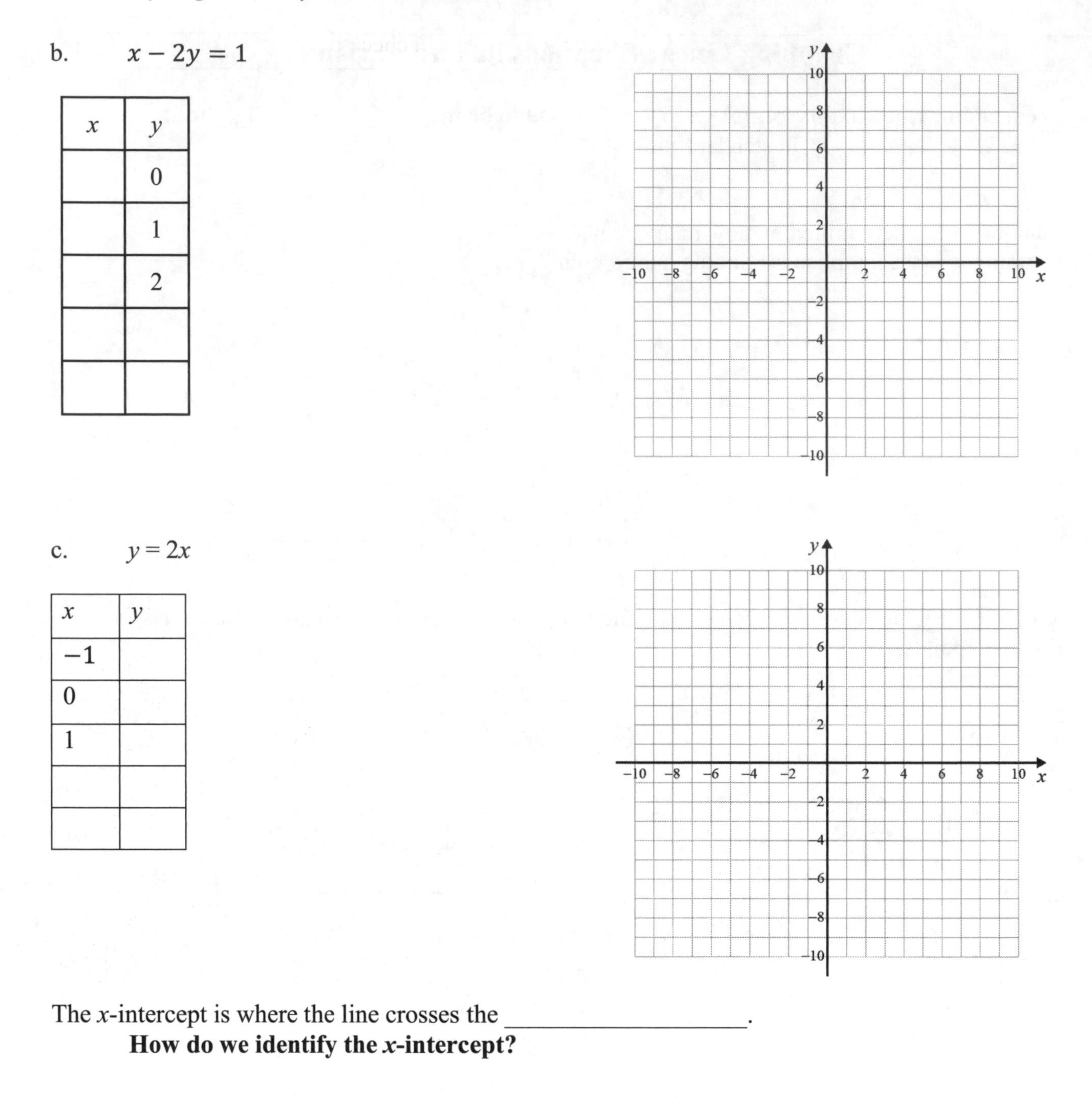

b. $x - 2y = 1$

x	y
	0
	1
	2

c. $y = 2x$

x	y
−1	
0	
1	

The x-intercept is where the line crosses the ____________________.

How do we identify the x-intercept?

The y-intercept is where the line crosses the ____________________.

How do we identify the y-intercept?

How can you tell from an equation that the line will go through the origin? When selecting points to graph it, what two picks would give you the same answer?

Make sure to fill in the third row of each table to create a check point. Two points make a line – a third point makes sure you have the right line!

Examples

Graph the following linear equations by locating the x- and y-intercepts.

2a. $x+3y=9$

x	y
0	
	0

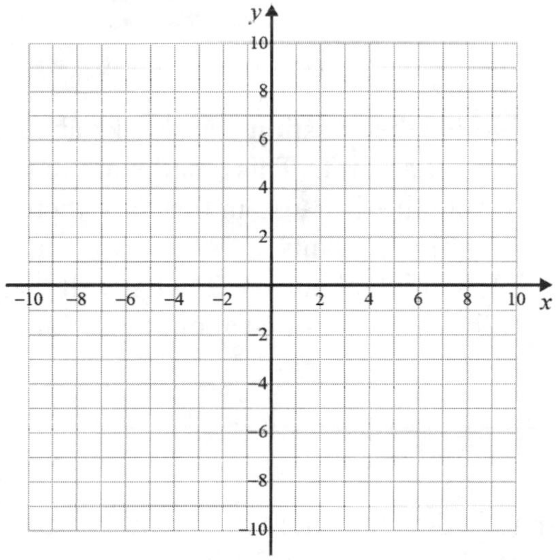

b. $3x - 2y = 12$

x	y
0	
	0

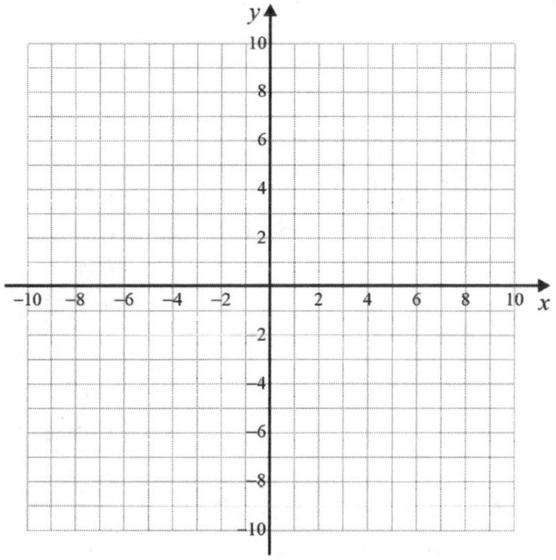

3. Graph $x - 5y = 5$ using the x- and y- intercepts.

x	y

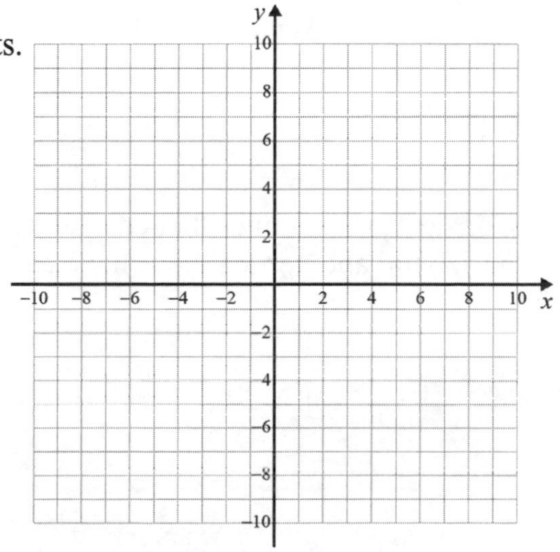

Horizontal and vertical lines have equations with only one variable.

What do you think the line $y=4$ will look like? Try making a table of values like above. What do you notice about the x-values in the table? About the y-values?

Notice the question above asks about a line even though $y=4$ might be misunderstood as a part of a point. This small equation tells you everything you need to know about the whole line because in this case there is no control over the missing variable, it can be anything it wants.

Now think about $x=-2$, what will that look like? Try making a table of values like above. What do you notice about the x-values in the table? About the y-values?

Summarize the characteristics about horizontal and vertical lines – thinking about direction, the intercepts, and points on the line.

Here is one mnemonic that may help to remember specifics of horizontal and vertical lines. Make sure that you can also draw both horizontal and vertical lines and connect the slope and equations to points on that graph.

VUX	HOY
Vertical	**H**orizontal
Undefined slope	Slope is **0**
$x = \#$	$y = \#$

Why does a vertical line have an equation $x=\#$ if it goes up and down?
Why does a horizontal line have an equation $y=\#$ if it goes left to right?

Considering that lines that are slanted have equations with both variables x and y, why do horizontal and vertical lines have equations with only one variable?

Examples

4. Graph the line: $y = 4$
   What is the coefficient of x?
   Create a chart for ordered pairs.

x	y

Graph the line.

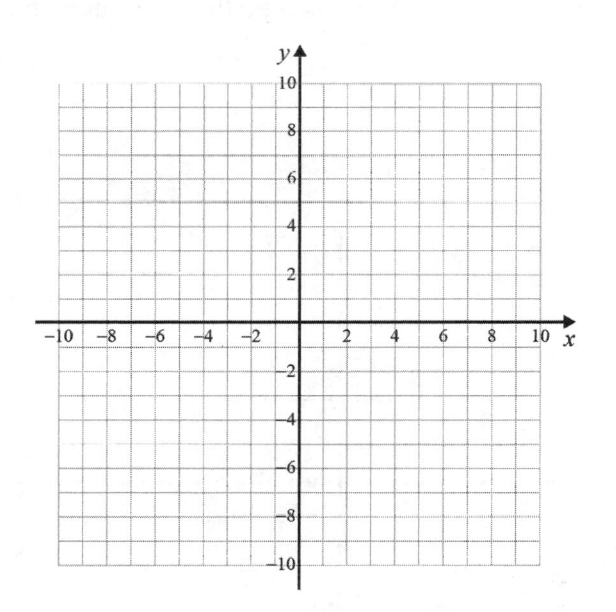

5. Graph the line: $x = -2$
   What is the coefficient of y?
   Create a chart for ordered pairs.

x	y

Graph the line.

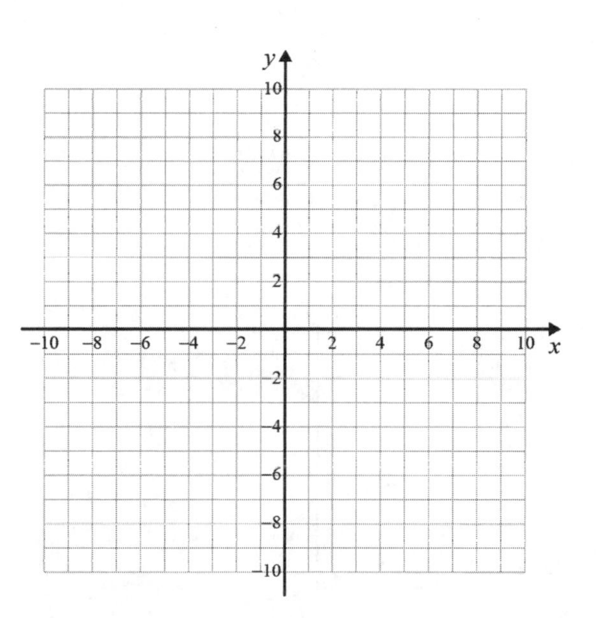

How can you tell by just looking at two ordered pairs if they are on a vertical or horizontal line?

Quick Quiz

Graph each equation using either the intercepts or arbitrary point method.

1. $x + y = 6$

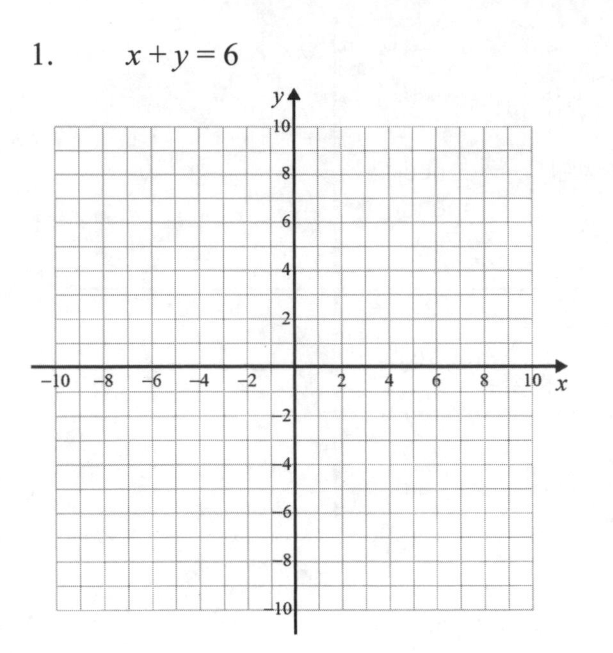

2. $\frac{3}{2}x - y = 2$

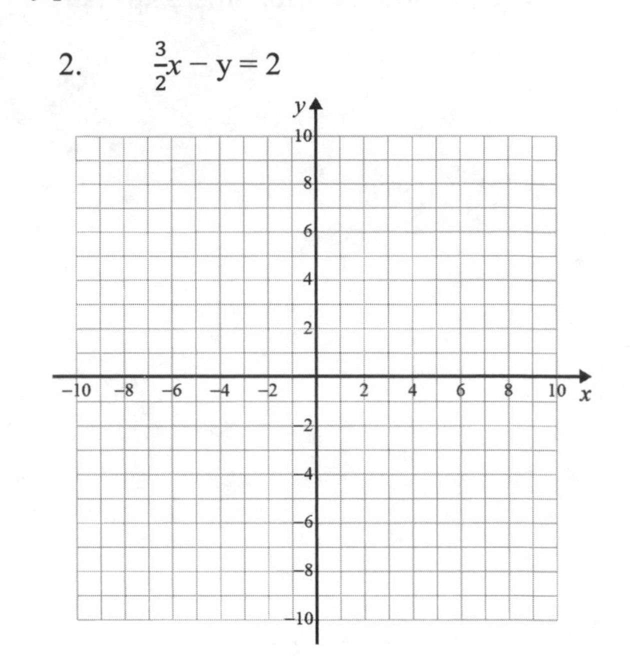

3. $x - 3 = 0$

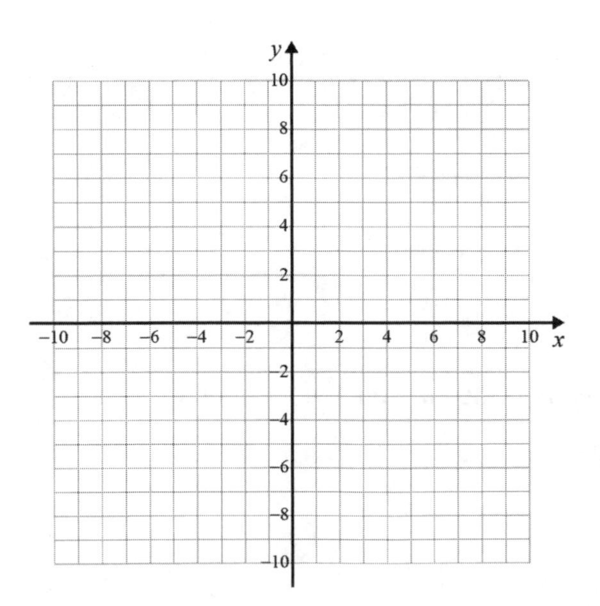

4. $y = 7$

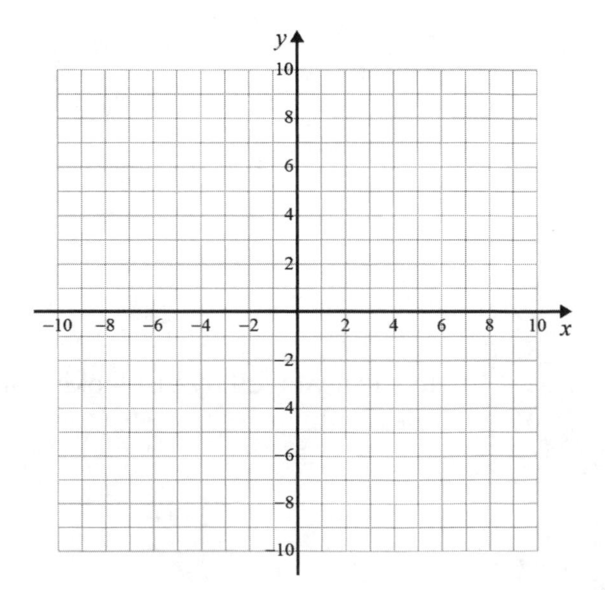

Slope

Slopes can be called several other names depending on what industry the problem describes.

What are some other names? ________________, ________________, ratio of ________________ to ______________, and rate of ________________.

Based on the terms above, describe other cases where the concept of slope is being implied. Thinking about time or money might generate some ideas.

The slope of the line is constant, meaning it will be the same regardless of which points from the line you use in the formula to calculate its value.

Slope Formula: $m = \frac{\text{rise}}{\text{run}} = \frac{y_2 - y_1}{x_2 - x_1}$

Examples

1. Find the slope of the line that goes through $(2, 6)$ and $(-3, 2)$.

$a - (-b)$ **is the same as** $a + b$

2. Find the slope of the line that contains the points $(-1, 2)$ and $(3, 5)$ and graph the line.

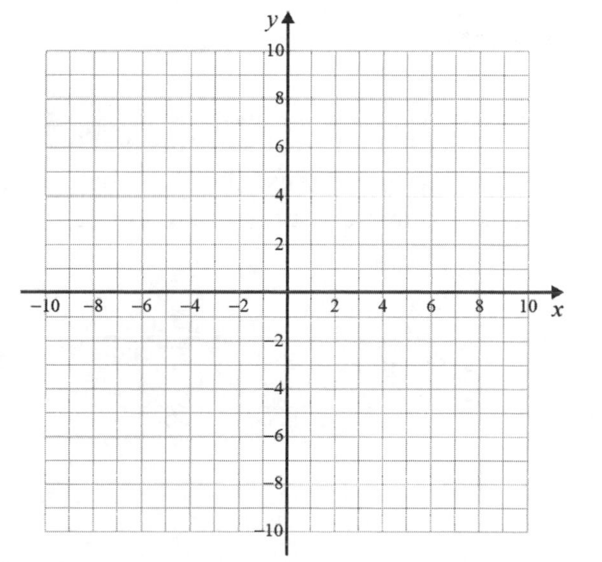

What happens if you put your pencil on (−1,2) and count rise over run to get to (3,5)?

3. Find the slope of the line that contains $(1, 3)$ and $(5, 1)$, and graph the line.

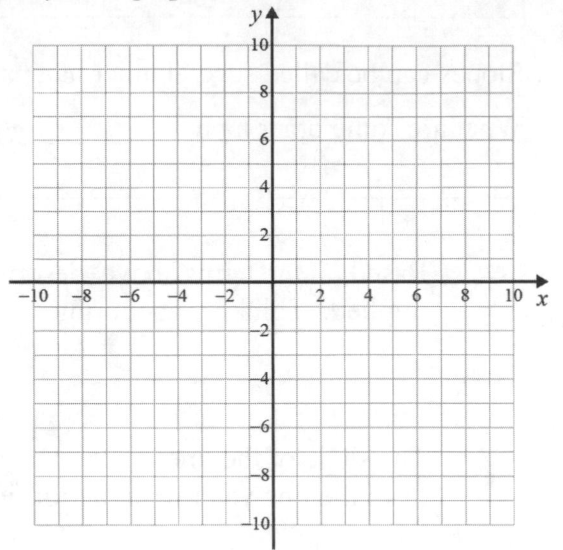

Lines that increase (go up) from left to right have ____________________ slopes.

Lines that decrease (go down) from left to right have ____________________ slopes.

Horizontal and Vertical Line Slopes

Consider the line that contains points $(-2, 3)$ and $(5, 3)$. Graph the line and use the slope formula to find the value of m. Compare your graph to your slope value.

Consider the line that contains points $(1, 3)$ and $(1, -2)$. Graph the line and use the slope formula to find the value of m. Compare your graph to your slope value.

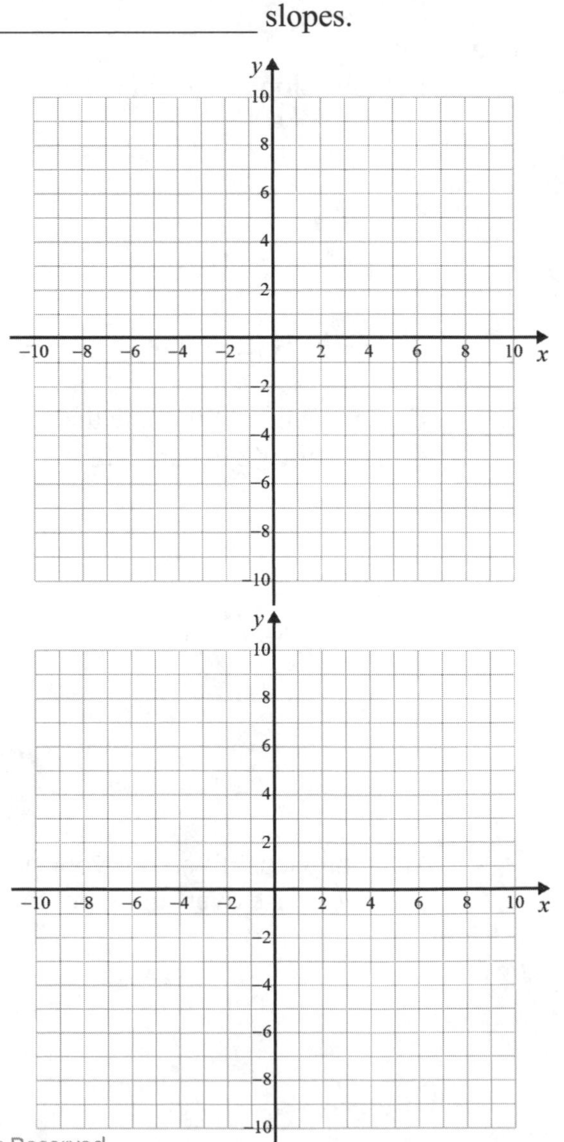

Every ______________________ line has slope of zero. (This line is said to have no rise.)

Every ______________________ line has ________________ slope. (This line is said to have no run.)

You can think about slopes like skiing. A steep slope is a quick rise. If you have a horizontal line, or no rise, you'll have 0 slope and go nowhere. If you have a vertical line and you try to ski down from the top you'll be undefined at the bottom!

Examples

Find the equation of the line and the slope for each, then graph the line.

4a. The horizontal line through point $(-2, 5)$ b. The vertical line through point $(3, 2)$

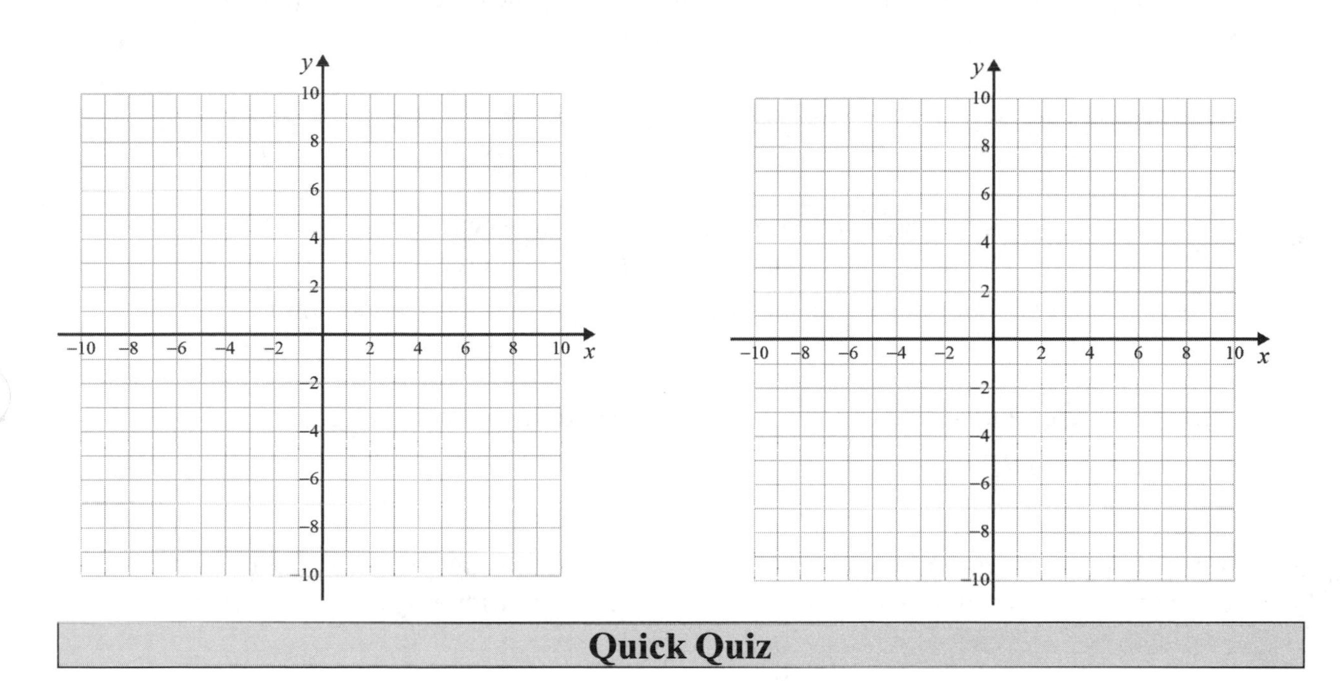

Quick Quiz

Find the slope of the line which contains each pair of points.

1. $(-4, 5)\ (2, 3)$
2. $(-\frac{3}{5}, 1)\ (-2, \frac{4}{7})$
3. $(5,0)\ \ (5,8)$
4. $(4, 3)\ \ (4, -5)$
5. $(\frac{3}{9}, -1)\ (-\frac{5}{6}, -\frac{1}{6})$
6. $(2,4)\ \ (-3,4)$

Slope-Intercept Form

Define **slope-intercept form** and define what each variable represents: x, y, m, and b.

The y-intercept describes a starting point for drawing a line and the slope gives us directions (rise and run) for getting to a second point on the graph. Not all lines go through the origin so you have to have a starting point when graphing.

If an equation is written in the standard form $Ax + By = C$, how do we write it in slope-intercept form?

Steps to graph a line using the slope-intercept form:

1. Put a point on the y-axis at b (the y-intercept).
2. From b, count the $\frac{\text{Rise}}{\text{Run}}$ using m (the slope) to find the second point.

How could you find a third point using the slope and the points you have?

What if you are counting your rise and run and go off the edge of your graph? Instead of extending your graph, how could you count your slope differently?

When working with fractions that are representing slope values, we can manipulate the negative signs when graphing. The fraction must always be equivalent to the original.

$-\frac{3}{4} = \frac{-3}{4}$ represents a rise of -3 and a run of 4 (line decreases from left to right)

$-\frac{3}{4} = \frac{3}{-4}$ represents a rise of 3 and a run of -4 (line decreases from left to right)

If given $m=\frac{3}{4}$, this can be written as $\frac{-3}{-4}$ for graphing. The values for the slope are the same.

Examples

Write the equation in slope-intercept form. Then give the slope, the y-intercept, and graph the line.

1a. $-2x + 3y = 6$

b. $x + 2y = -6$

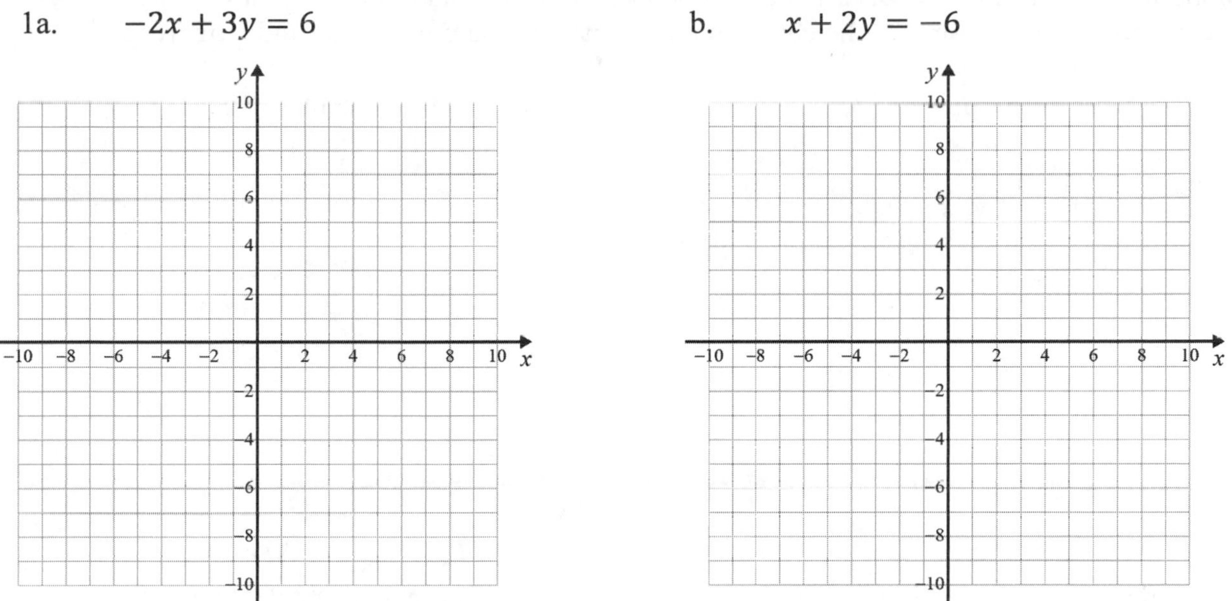

How do you write the equation of a line given the slope and y-intercept?

When given ordered pairs of points on the line, how do you know if one of them is the y-intercept? And if one is, where would the value of "b" come from?

Examples

2. Find the equation of the line...

a. that contains $(0, 1)$ with slope 3.

b. that contains $(0, -2)$ with slope $\frac{1}{2}$.

When given two points on a line, how do you write the equation of a line when you don't have the slope?

3. Find the equation, in slope-intercept form, of the line that goes through $(0, -1)$ and $(2, 3)$.

Quick Quiz

The slope-intercept form of an equation can be found if the slope and y-intercept are both known. Write the slope-intercept form of the equation represented by the given slope and y-intercept.

1. $m = -2$; y-intercept $= (0,12)$

2. $m = 0$; y-intercept $= (0,3)$

3. $m = \frac{4}{5}$; y-intercept $= (0,-\frac{1}{2})$

4. $m =$ undefined; x-intercept $(3,0)$

Point-Slope Form

Just as two points define a unique line, a point and a slope also define a unique line. Remember that you must always have a "starting point" for any line. The slope gives you directions but you need to know where to start first.

Examples

1. Graph the line with slope $-\frac{3}{4}$ that passes through the point $(2, 5)$.

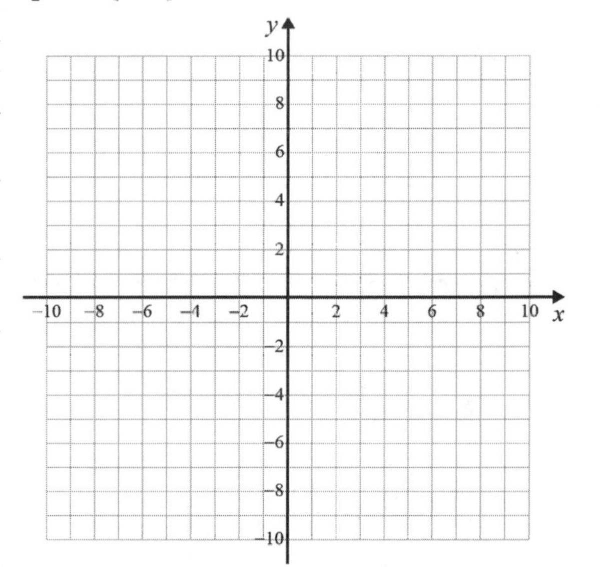

Name two other points that would be on the line other than (2,5). How did you find those?

If the starting point for this line had been (−2,8) would the line have graphed as the same line? Why or why not?

One method already used was to write the equation of a line using slope and y-intercept. The form $y=mx+b$ can be used for writing all equations of lines but may require a few extra steps with algebraic manipulation to find the result. What if we knew two points on the line but not the slope? Here is another option.

Define **Point-Slope Form** and define what each variable represents: x, y, x_1, y_1, m, and b. What information must you have in order to apply this method for writing an equation?

Use the example demonstrated to list the steps for finding the equation of a line given a slope and a point on the line. Example: $(x_1, y_1) = (8, 3)$ and $m = -\frac{3}{4}$.

Examples

2. Use the point-slope form to find the equation of the line with slope of $-\frac{1}{2}$ that passes through the point $(2, 3)$. Write the equation in slope-intercept form and in standard form. Graph the line and pick a point on the line to test your equation.

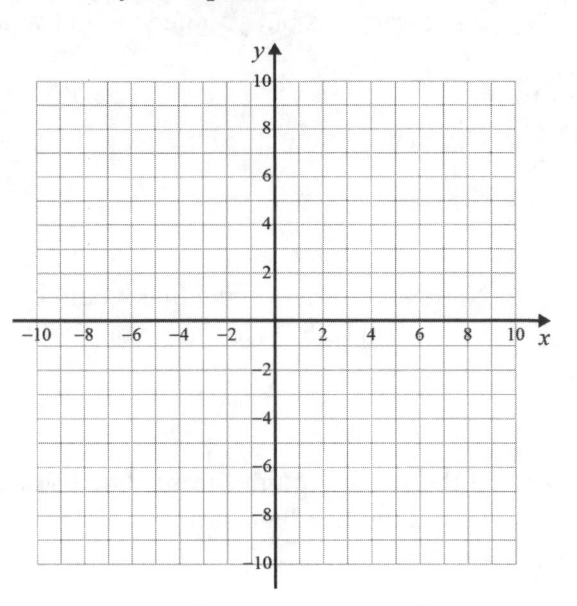

Steps to find the equation of a line given two points.

1.

2.

In step 2 only **one** of the points is used. Try example 3 twice using a different point each time and see what happens.

Examples

3. Find the equation of the line containing the two points $(-1, 2)$ and $(4, -2)$.

Using (−1,2) as your point.	Using (4,−2) as your point.

Quick Quiz

1. Write the equation $y = 14x + 2$ in standard form and graph the line.

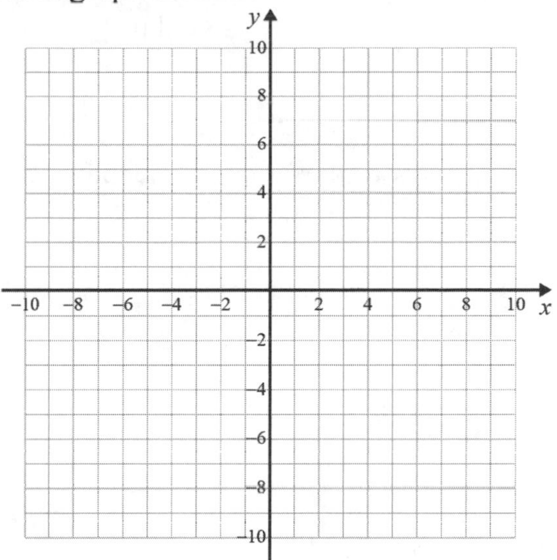

2. Find the equation of the line that goes through points $(2, -1)$ and $(3, 1)$.

Parallel and Perpendicular Lines

Define and draw an example of **parallel** lines. What is the symbol for parallel?

Define and draw an example of **perpendicular** lines. What is the symbol for perpendicular?

What is the relationship between the slopes of parallel lines?

What is the relationship between the slopes of perpendicular lines?

Sketch the cases below to support your answer.
If $m = 2$ for a given line, …

the slope of the line parallel to it will be $m =$

the slope of the line perpendicular to it will be $m =$

If $m = \frac{2}{3}$ for a given line,…

the slope of the line parallel to it will be $m =$

the slope of the line perpendicular to it will be $m =$

If two lines are graphed on the same coordinate plane (flat 2-dimensional), then those two lines do one of three things. They are parallel, they cross (intersect), or they cross perpendicularly. Perpendicular lines are intersecting but are a special case.

If given two equations of lines, without graphing how do you determine if the lines are parallel, perpendicular, or intersecting? Fill in the table below indicating if the two lines would have the same or different values to help before writing steps.

	Parallel	Intersecting	Perpendicular
Graph			
Slope			
y-intercepts			

Now, how would you take two equations and determine their relationship?

Describe the steps for finding the equation of a line when given a parallel or perpendicular reference line and a point for the line.

Examples

1. Find the equation of the line through the point $(2, 3)$ and parallel to $5x + 3y = 1$.

2. Find the equation of the line through the point $(2, 3)$ and perpendicular to the line $5x + 3y = 1$.

Once you find the slope of the original reference line and use it to determine your new slope, you are finished with the reference line. You then focus on writing the new equation using your new slope and the given points.

Summarize your properties and formulas related to writing equations of a line. Work to connect the different formulas together and make notes.

Formula	Property	Notes
	Standard Form	
	Slope of a Line	
	Slope-Intercept From	
	Point-Slope Form	
	Horizontal Line, slope = ____	
	Vertical Line, slope is ______	
	Have the same slope	
	Have slopes that are negative reciprocals of each other	

Quick Quiz

1. Write the equation of the line parallel to $2x - y = -1$ through the point (0,3).

2. Find the equation of the line perpendicular to $3x + 2y = -1$ through the point (1,4).

Determine the relationship between the pairs of equations. Identify each pair as parallel, perpendicular, or "just" intersecting. Justify your answer. (What should your first step be?)

4. $y = \frac{1}{2}x + 7$ and $y = 2x - 15$

5. $y = \frac{-6}{7}x - 50$ and $y = \frac{7}{6}x + 2$

6. $y = \frac{2}{5}x + 5$ and $-2x + 5y = 10$

7. $2x + 7y = 14$ and $5x + 7y = 14$

Graphing Linear Inequalities in Two Variables

What is the difference between a linear equation and a linear inequality?

Given an equation is $y=3x+2$ and an inequality is $y>3x+2$, what is the general relationship between x and y being described by each?

How would the solutions to each be represented on the graph?

Given the point (1,5), would this point be a solution to the equation? How about to the inequality? Why?

Given the point (0,4), would this point be a solution to the equation? How about to the inequality? Why?

Given the point (2,5), would this point be a solution to the equation? How about to the inequality? Why?

Linear inequalities can be represented as an area of the Cartesian plane bounded by a line. What is a **boundary line**?

When should the boundary line be dotted?
Does this create an open or closed half-plane?
Are the points on the line a solution to the inequality?

When should the boundary line be solid?
Does this create an open or closed half-plane?
Are the points on the line a solution to the inequality?

What is a **half-plane**? What does the shaded area actually represent? Does a half-plane stop at the edge of the graph paper?

Don't forget that when solving an inequality for y, if you multiply or divide by a negative number the inequality symbol reverses, so $>$ becomes $<$ and vice versa.

Steps to Graph Linear Inequalities:

1. Graph the line and determine whether to use a dotted line or a solid line.

Dotted (Open) =	Solid (Closed) =

2. Determine which side of the line needs to be shaded.

   Method 1:

   Method 2:

How do we determine which half-plane to shade for a vertical inequality?

Examples

Graph the half-plane that satisfies the inequality:

1a. $2x + y \leq 6$

b. $y > 2x$

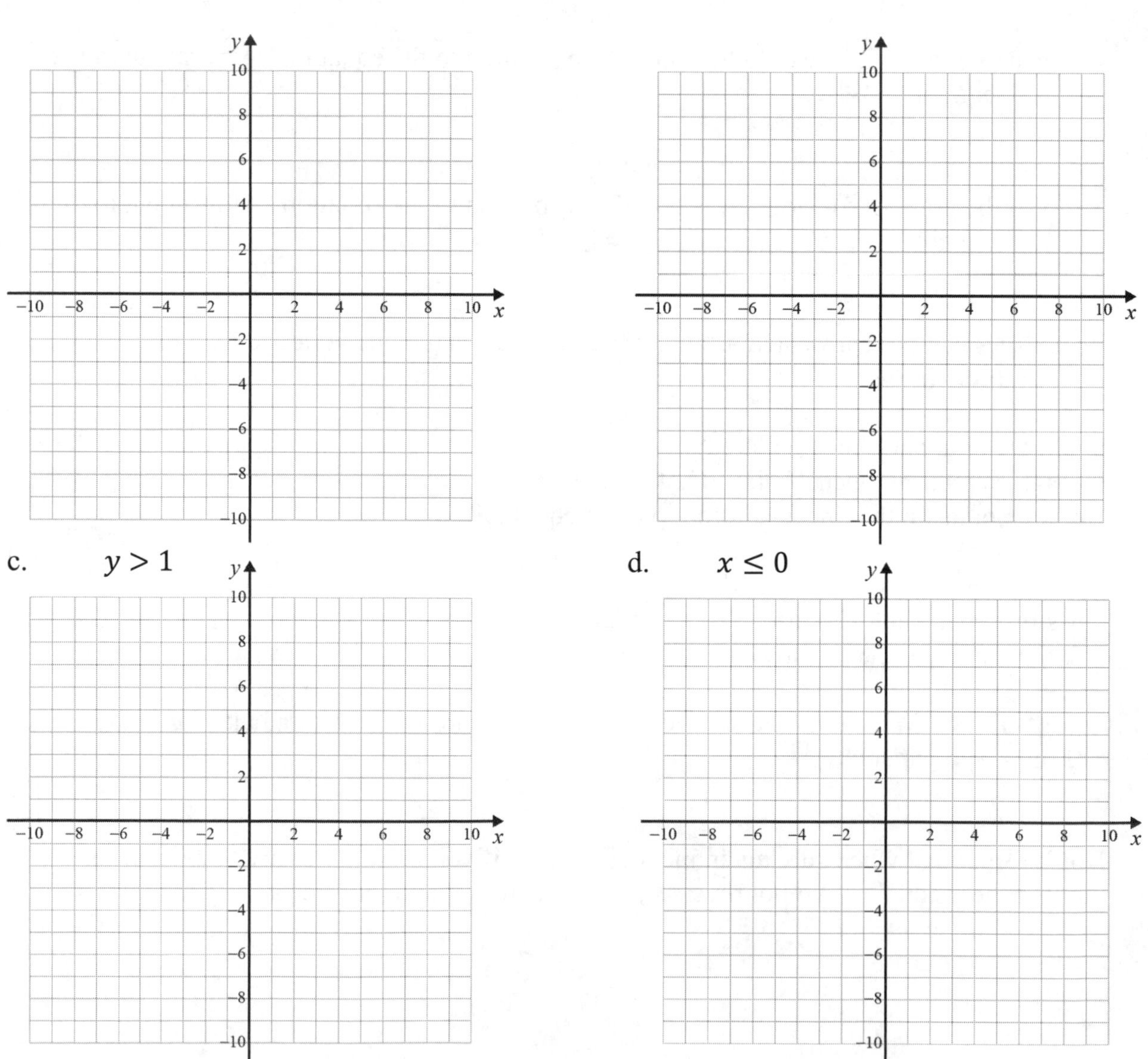

c. $y > 1$

d. $x \leq 0$

Which method will you use to find the shaded area? Why?

Quick Quiz

Graph the following.

1. $2x - 4y \geq 12$

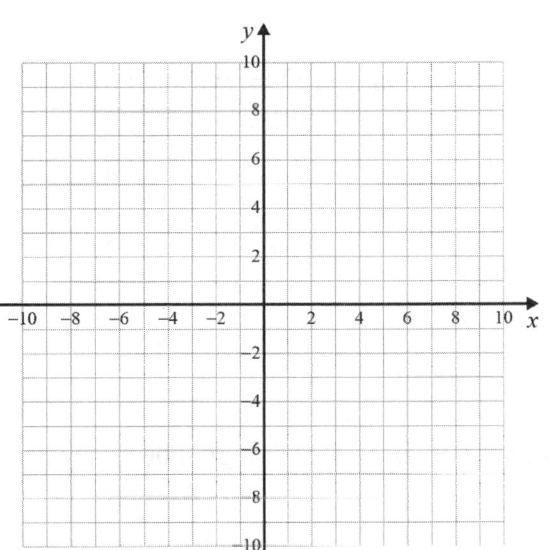

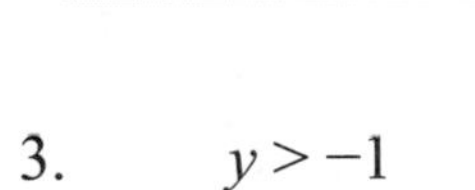

2. $4x < -3y + 9$

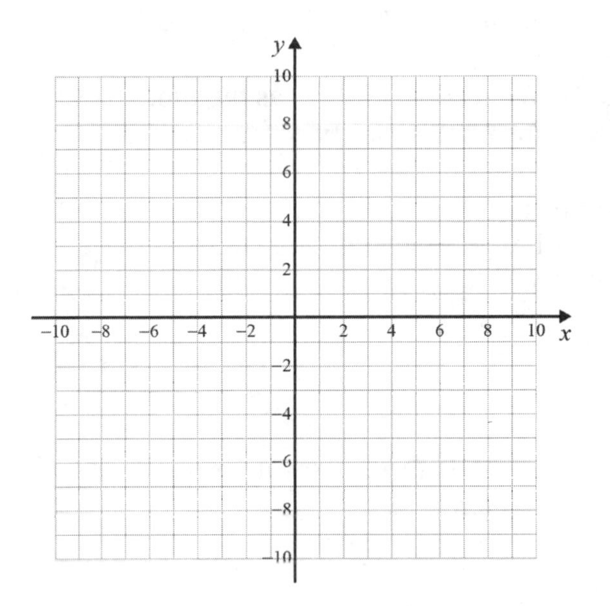

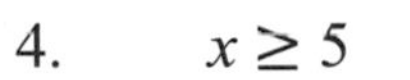

3. $y > -1$

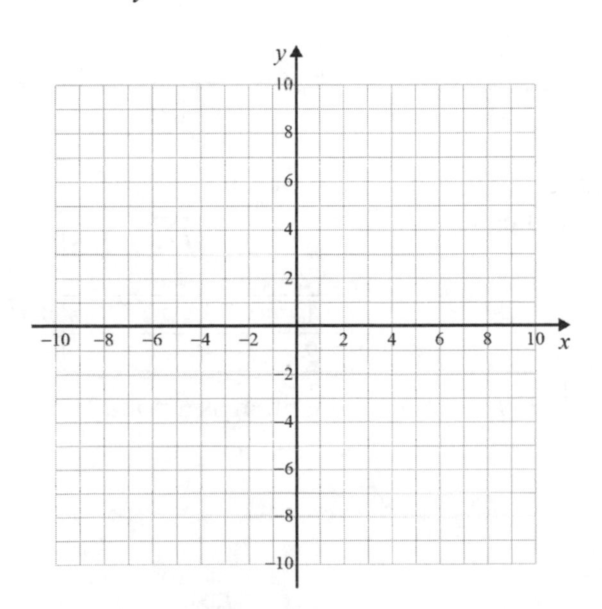

4. $x \geq 5$

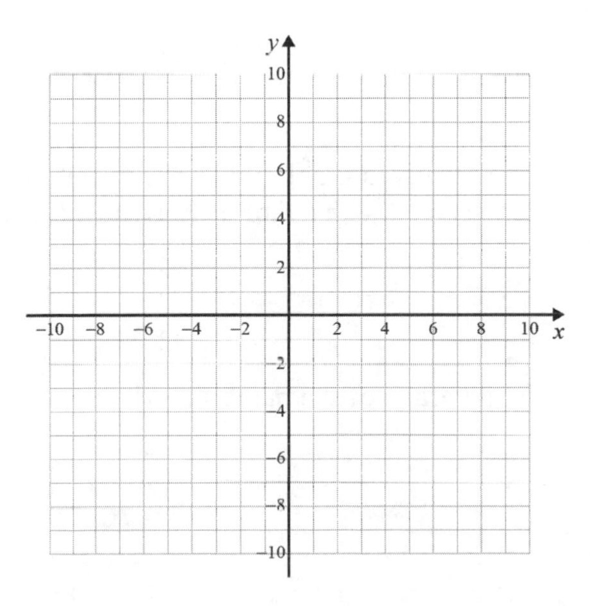

Introduction to Functions and Function Notation

An equation is a relationship between two variables, usually x and y. But when a relationship is special resulting in exactly one y value for each x value, it is said to be a function. Function notation, $f(x)$, is used to indicate that not only is there a relationship between x and y, there is a special relationship that is dependent on the variable "x".

Write $y = 2x + 5$ using function notation.

How do we read the function $f(x) = 2x + 5$?

Using the function $f(x) = 2x + 5$, what is $f(3) =$ ____________________?

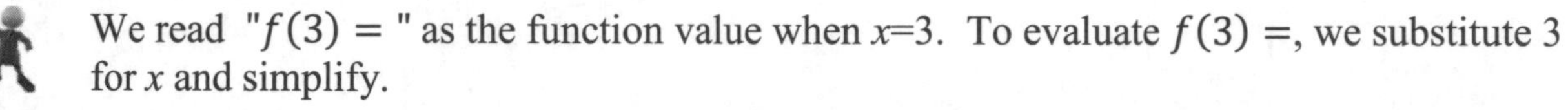

We read "$f(3) =$ " as the function value when x=3. To evaluate $f(3) =$, we substitute 3 for x and simplify.

Examples

1. For $g(x) = -2x - 1$, find

   a. $g(2)$ b. $g(0)$

What do these two values represent? How else can the values of g(2) and g(0) be written?

2. For $h(x) = x^2 - 4x + 3$, find

   a. $h(1)$ b. $h(-2)$

Use the given graph of a curve to complete the table. How can these values be represented with a table? Rewrite these as an ordered pair.

x	$y = f(x)$
-2	
1	
2	

In the graph of the parabola, why does $f(-2) = 5$? How can this be written as a point?

3. Find the function values. Sketch the graph to the right and plot the function values as defined below.

   a. $g(0)$
   b. $g(2)$
   c. $g(4)$

4. Use the graph to determine the value for x for each of the following:

   a. $g(x)=-3$ b. $g(x)=0$ c. $g(x)=2$

What is $g(x)=-3$ asking? Write a sentence that restates this question.

What would this chart look like for example 4 above?

x	$y = g(x)$

Quick Quiz

Evaluate the functions for the given values.

1. $f(x) = x^2 - 5$

   a. $f(2)$ b. $f(-3)$

2. $g(x) = \frac{10-x}{3}$

   a. $g(25)$ b. $g(-7)$

Systems of Linear Equations: Solutions by Graphing

What is a **system of equations**?

The solution of a system of two linear equations is an ordered pair that satisfies ____________ equations.

How is the solution expressed?

How do you check that an ordered pair is a solution to the system?

Examples

1, Show that $(2, 1)$ is the solution to the system $x - 2y = 0$ and $3x + y = 7$.

2. Show that $(0,4)$ is NOT the solution to the system $y = -x + 4$ and $y = 2x + 1$.

In this module, we will discuss 3 methods that can be used to solve a system of linear equations.

1. By Graphing
2. By Substitution
3. By Addition (Linear Combination or Subtraction)

When solving graphically, how is the solution determined?

Types of systems and solutions:

Define **consistent**.

Define **inconsistent**.

Define **dependent**.

Define **independent**.

As you work through examples, complete the table summarizing solutions to different systems.

Remember: m is the slope of a line and b is the y-intercept. A box in a corner indicates 90 degrees.

Graph				
Coincide, Parallel, Perpendicular, or Intersecting				
Slopes				
y-Intercepts				
Consistent or Inconsistent				
Dependent or Independent				
# of Solutions				
Notes				

Work to make a connection between the graphs and the meaning of the different terms. Make notes to remind yourself of these connections.

Solving system of equations graphically.
Describe the steps for graphing a system and identifying the solution.

Remember: The 3 methods to graph a line are

1. **Plot points**: Create ordered pairs by choosing random values for x or y and solving for the other variable.
2. Find the **x- and y- intercepts**: Set $x = 0$ and solve for y. Then set $y = 0$ and solve for x.
3. Use the **slope-intercept** form: Plot the y-intercept "b" on the y-axis, then count the $\frac{\text{Rise}}{\text{Run}}$ using the slope m.

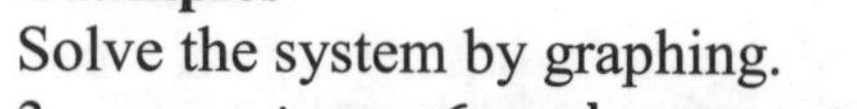

Examples

Solve the system by graphing.

3. $x + y = 6$ and $y = x + 4$

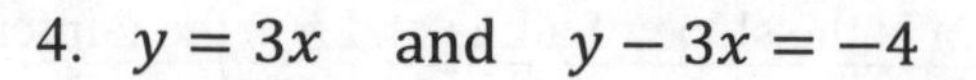

4. $y = 3x$ and $y - 3x = -4$

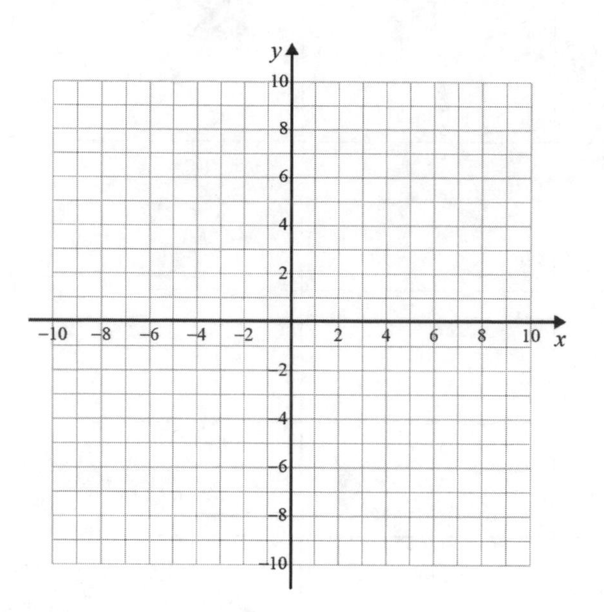

Check your solution in both equations.

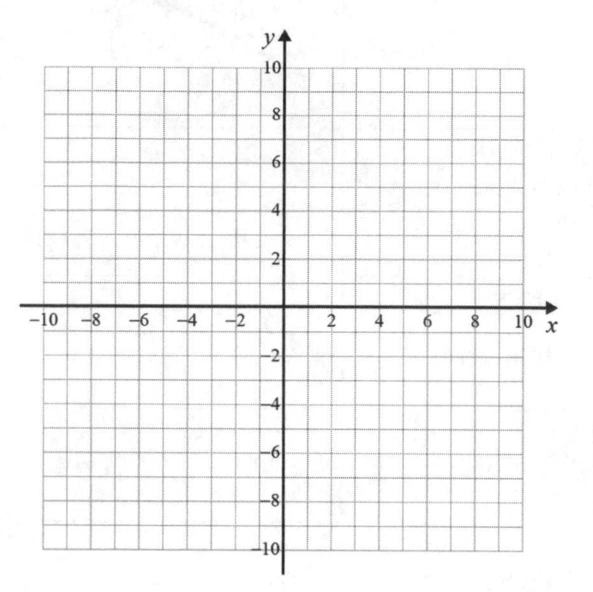

Check your solution in both equations.

5. $x + 2y = 6$ and $y = -\frac{1}{2}x + 3$

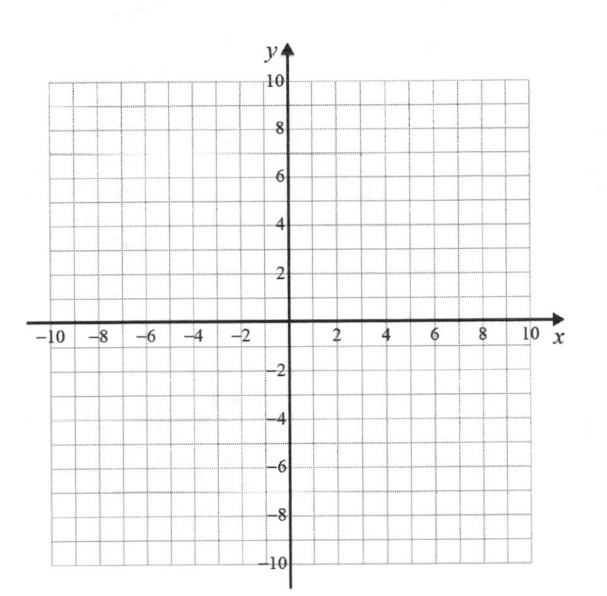

Check your solution in both equations.

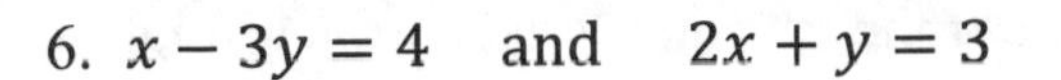

6. $x - 3y = 4$ and $2x + y = 3$

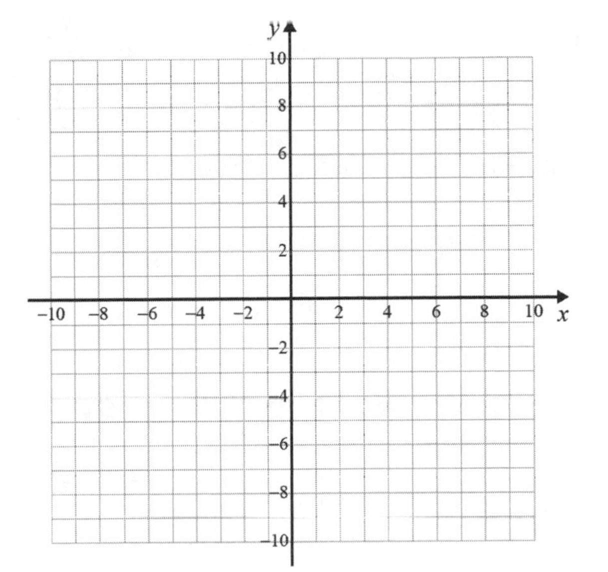

Check your solution in both equations.

Why might the graphing method not be the best method to use all the time? What difficulties might arise when solving by graphing?

If a solution works in one equation in the system does it have to automatically work in the other? Why or why not? If not, what would it look like graphically to have it work in one but not the other? Sketch an example.

Quick Quiz

Determine if the given ordered pair is a solution to the equation.

1. $x - y = 4$ $(1, -3)$
   $3x - y = 6$

2. $4x = 3 + y$ $(2, 6)$
   $x + 8 = 2y$

Determine if the system is consistent or inconsistent and describe it as dependent or independent. Justify your answer.

What form of the equations makes the slope and y-intercept obvious?

3. $2x + y = 3$
   $2x + y = 5$

What are two ways you might deal with the fraction in the second equation below?

4. $3x - y = 8$
   $x - \frac{1}{3}y = 2$

Solve by graphing.

5. $4x + 2y = -4$
   $4x + 2y = -20$

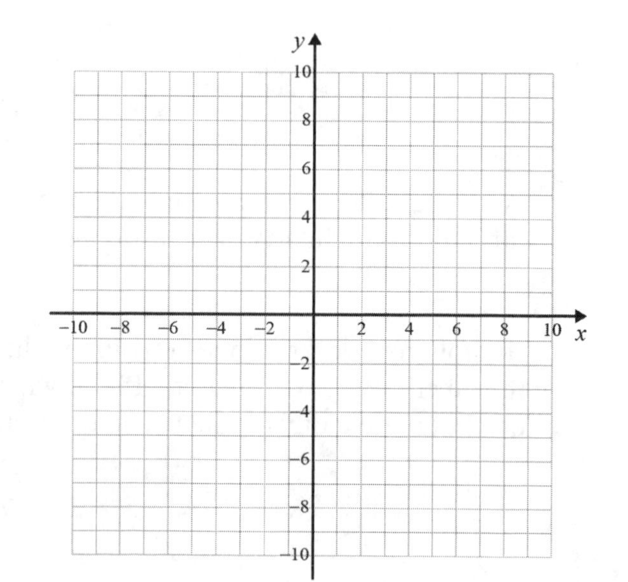

Systems of Linear Equations: Solutions by Substitution

In the previous section, we learned how to solve a system by ______________________. In this section, we will discuss solving a system using the substitution method.

Steps to solve a system using the **substitution method.**

1.

2.

3.

4.

After you have solved one equation for a given variable, where should you substitute the found value to continue to solve? What would happen if you substituted back into the equation you just used to isolate the variable?

Under what conditions is the substitution method most often used?

Examples

Solve the system using the substitution method. Show the check for your solutions.

We can isolate any variable to use this method. In example 2, why might you choose the "y" in the first equation to isolate versus any other variable in the problem?

1. $y = \frac{5}{6}x + 2$ and $\frac{1}{6}x + y = 8$

2. $3x + y = 1$ and $6x + 2y = 3$

Which variable is the easiest to isolate in example 3? Why would you want to avoid solving for the y in either equation?

3. $x - 2y = 1$ and $3x - 6y = 3$

In examples 2 and 3, we saw that sometimes the variables subtract or cancel-out, leaving a statement that is either true or false.

If the statement is **true**, the resulting solution is what? Describe what is happening graphically in this case.

When you have infinitely many pair of solutions, you can express that solution in the form of an equation. Remember from graphing that this is a case when the two lines coincide or are exactly the same. Which means the two equations are exactly the same. If we solve both equations for $y=$ we get the same equation, like in example 2, the result is $y=1-3x$. So better than just saying there are infinitely many pairs, we can add "that satisfy the equation $y=1-3x$." It is important to realize that infinitely many pairs does not mean any random point on the graph works. It has to be a point on that line.

If the statement is **false**, the resulting solution is what? Describe what is happening graphically in this case.

Examples

Solve the system using the substitution method. Show the check for your solutions.

4. $x + y = 5$ and $0.2x + 0.3y = 0.9$

What is a benefit to eliminating decimals? Do you have to remove decimals to solve this system?

5. $x + y = 3$ and $2x - y = 12$

Quick Quiz

Solve the system using the substitution method. Show the check for your solutions.

1. $x+y=6$
   $x+y=7$

2. $2x+5y=15$
   $x=y-3$

3. $x-2y=-4$
   $3x+y=-5$

4. $6x-y=15$
   $18x-45=3y$

Systems of Linear Equations: Solutions by Addition

We have learned to use two methods to solve a system of linear equations in the previous sections. List each method and state when that method is best applied.

1.

2.

Steps to use the **addition method**:

1.

2.

3.

4.

5.

Examples

Use the addition method to solve the system. Show your check for the solution.

Example 1 is solved by eliminating the y. What would be the first step if you wanted to eliminate the x instead?

1. $3x + 5y = -3$
   $-7x + 2y = 7$

2. $3x - \frac{1}{2}y = 6$
   $6x - y = 12$

3. $x + 0.4y = 3.08$
   $0.1x - y = 0.1$

4. $x - y = -1$
   $2x + 3y = 33$

Review the examples that resulted in a solution of **infinite number of pairs** in the sections regarding systems. Thinking back to the table of system properties, explain how you can find a relationship between the two original equations **before** you solve them.

In the next section, we will be creating systems of equations to solve application problems. Since you have learned three methods to solve these systems, you will be able to choose which method you want to use. Note the guidelines for making that choice:

1.

2.

3.

4.

Quick Quiz

Use the addition method to solve the system. Show your check for the solution.

1. $2x + \frac{1}{3}y = -10$
   $6x - 7y = 3$

2. $6x - 5y = -40$
   $8x - 7y = -54$

3. $0.75x - 0.5y = 2$
   $1.5x - 0.75y = 7.5$

4. $10x + 4y = 7$
   $5x + 2y = 15$

Applications: Distance-Rate-Time, Number Problems, Amounts, and Costs

The problems in this section are examples of the endless list of applications. You will be expected to apply what you learned in these examples to other types of questions. Pay attention to **how** problems are set up as well as how to solve so that you can apply these skills to a broader spectrum of applications.

Remember that "per" or "each" indicates a rate. Slope is also called the "rate of change." Therefore, use references to the rate as clues to the slope.

With many applications the basic idea of finding a total value applies.
(Quantity)(Rate or value of each) = Total Value

Anytime you are setting up equations make sure…

- you define your variables – what is each variable standing for? Use letters that make sense to you.
- as you fill in the blocks, more than one piece of information may be needed. For example, the quantity might be boys + girls not just one or the other.
- that the left and right side of the equations are representing the same concept.
- each equation can represent a different type of total but the variables must always represent the same thing. Equation 1 total tickets, equation 2 total cost.
- each equation represents a case or type of total. (Often its own sentence in your application. But sometimes it is implied.)
- for each variable, you must have an equation in order to solve. 2 variables = 2 equations.
- upon solving your system state your answer in a sentence and check it for reasonableness.

A **table** is often used to help you organize your information and create your equations.

Case	Quantity	Rate or value of each	Total Value
Case 1	•	=	
Case 2	•	=	

Sometimes you may have more than one pair of (Quantity)(Value) in which case you can add more columns. For example if you wanted your total grocery bill…
(LBS meat)(price meat) + (LBS veg)(price veg) + (#boxes cereal)(price per box)… = total bill

Writing these types of word equations can also help you organize your thoughts.

Two of the formulas in this and the next section are $I = Prt$ and $D = rt$. What is similar about the formulas? How do they relate to the table above?

A table is not always necessary for solving an application or system. Some applications can be solved using **translations.**

Some hints for using translations to create equations:

- define all variables first, using letters that make sense to you.
- **is** means =, **of** means multiply, **per** means divide.
- **sum** means add, **difference** means subtract, **product** means multiply, and **quotient** means divide. All four indicate ( ) are needed.
- review other vocabulary from your earlier work or look up words for which you are unsure of their meaning.
- the words "**than**" and "**from**" indicate the numbers should be reversed when written. 3 from 8 is $8-3$
- typically each sentence represents its own equation.
- just like in your English studies, prepositional phrases usually add support information but not critical information to the equation. Don't confuse "of" as multiply and "of" the preposition.
- translate each sentence or case into an equation. Remember that 2 variables means there are 2 equations to create the system.
- upon solving your system state your answer in a sentence and check it for reasonableness.

These are just two major strategies for solving applications; there are other approaches. The keys in any strategy are to make sense of what you are doing, understand the question, and make sure to answer what is asked. Sometimes common sense is the best strategy of all.

Examples

Solve each application. Define your variables, determine your equations, solve, state your answer in a sentence, and check for reasonableness of your answer.

1. A small plane flew 300 miles in 2 hours flying with the wind. Then on the return trip, flying against the wind, it traveled only 200 miles in 2 hours. What were the wind speed and the speed of the plane with no wind?

2. Two buses leave a bus station traveling in opposite directions. One leaves at noon and the second leaves at 1 p.m. The first one travels at an average speed of 55 mph and the second one at an average speed of 59 mph. At what time will the buses be 226 miles apart?

3. The sum of two numbers is 80 and their difference is 10. What are the two numbers?

4. Mike has \$1.05 worth of change in nickels and quarters. If he has twice as many nickels as quarters, how many of each type of coin does he have?

5. Kathy is 6 years older than her sister, Sue. In 3 years, she will be twice as old as Sue. How old is each girl now?

6. Three hot dogs and two orders of French fries cost \$10.30. Four hot dogs and four orders of fries cost \$15.60. What is the cost of a hot dog? What is the cost of an order of fries?

Quick Quiz

A carnival charges \$5 for children and \$10 for adults. On Tuesday, the carnival made \$1400 from ticket sales and sold a total of 200 tickets. How many adults and how many children visited the carnival?

1. Define the variables.
2. Define the appropriate number of equations.
3. Solve and state your answer in a sentence. Show all of the work you did to obtain the solution. (If done in your head, explain your thinking here.)
4. Check for reasonableness of your answer.

Applications: Interest and Mixture

Review your solving application notes from the prior lesson. These strategies and rules apply to any type of applications.

The use of formulas is also helpful in solving applications.
Formulas relate different variables using mathematics. When some of the values for the variables are known, a formula can be used to find the value of what is needed.
When using formulas make sure to…

- Define your variables. What does each variable mean?
- Substitute values for the variables that you know.
- Use order of operations and/or steps for solving equations to solve for the desired variable.
- Check your answer by plugging all values back into the formula.
- State your answer in a sentence and confirm reasonableness.

In the formula $I = Prt$, give the meaning of each variable:

P	
r	
t	
I	

What does it mean that *Prt* are all side by side?

Examples
Solve each application. Define your variables, determine your equations, solve, state your answer in a sentence, and check for reasonableness of your answer.

1. James has two investment accounts, one pays 6% interest and the other pays 10% interest. He has $1000 more in the 10% account than he has in the 6% account. In one year, the interest from the 10% account is $260 more than the interest from the 6% account. How much does he have in each account?

2. Lila has $7000 to invest. She decides to separate her funds into two accounts. One yields interest at the rate of 7% and the other at 12%. If she wants a total annual income from both accounts to be $690, how should she split the money?

3. How many ounces each of a 10% salt solution and a 15% salt solution must be used to produce 50 ounces of a 12% salt solution?

4. How many gallons of a 20% acid solution should be mixed with a 30% acid solution to produce 100 gallons of a 23% solution?

Quick Quiz

Sanjay has $5000 to invest and he has an option to split the amount between two simple interest accounts. Account A is expected to earn 4% interest and Account B is expected to earn 9% interest. Sanjay has a goal to make $350 in interest after one year. How much should he invest in each account?

1. Define the variables.
2. Define the appropriate number of equations.
3. Solve and state your answer in a sentence. Show all of the work you did to obtain the solution. (If done in your head, explain your thinking here.)
4. Check for reasonableness of your answer.

Vocabulary Check

Define each of the following terms in your own words, providing examples as necessary to clarify the term.

Boundary line

Slope

Coordinate

Quadrant

Dependent variable

Variable

Function notation

Origin

Horizontal line

Vertical line

Independent variable

Solution set

Infinite

Subscript

Intercepts

Point-slope formula

Linear equation

Half-plane

Parallel

Standard form

Perpendicular

Slope-intercept form

$D=rt$

$I=Prt$

System

Concept Review

Answer the following questions as completely as possible in your own words. Make sure to get the big points of each with key steps involved.

1. What are the parts of the coordinate plane?

2. What is an ordered pair?

3. What are the x-intercepts and y-intercepts and how do you find them?

4. How do you graph a line using x- and y-intercepts?

5. How do you graph a line using slope-intercept form?

6. What does slope mean?

7. How do you find slope from:
   a. a graph

   b. two points

   c. from an equation

8. What is slope-intercept form of a linear equation?

9. What is standard form of a linear equation?

10. How do you write an equation of a line using slope-intercept form?

11. What is function notation?

12. How do you evaluate a function?

13. What does it mean if the system is independent or dependent?

14. What does it mean if the system is consistent or inconsistent?

15. What are the three ways to find a solution to a system of equations? When would you use each?

16. How do you know when lines are parallel or perpendicular?

17. How do you determine which side of the line to shade when graphing a linear inequality?

18. What are the three application problem formulas from this section that you need to memorize?

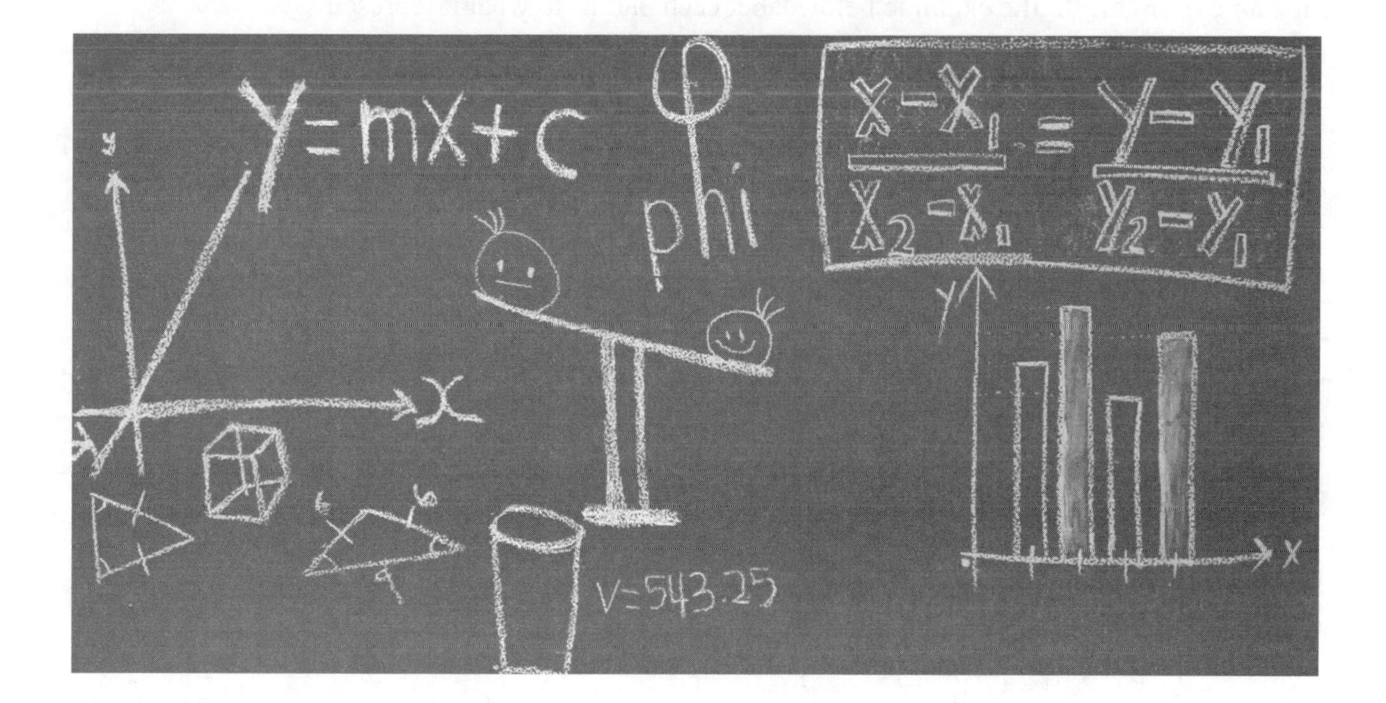

Unit 6

Exponents, Factoring, and Polynomial Equations

Exponents

Define an **exponent**. In the example below label each part as to what it represents.

$$6^2 \quad = \quad 6 \cdot 6 \quad = \quad 36$$

Product Rule for Exponents
When multiplying two exponential terms, the bases are matched and the exponents are added.

Use the example $m^3 \cdot m^4$ and show why the product rule works by both expanding the exponents and also by applying the product rule. Are the answers the same?

Examples
Simplify each expression. If no exponent is shown, it is understood to be 1. ($a = a^1$)

1a. $x^2 \cdot x^4$ b. $y \cdot y^6$ c. $4^2 \cdot 4$

d. $2^3 \cdot 2^2$ e. $(-2)^4(-2)^3$

When we multiply terms, we multiply the numerical coefficients. Apply the product rule only to the exponents with like bases.

2a. $2y^2 \cdot 3y^9$ b. $(-3x^3)(-4x^3)$ c. $(-6ab^2)(8ab^3)$

The expression $0^0 =$ _______.
Any other nonzero real number raised to the zero power equals?

If 6^4 is $6{\times}6{\times}6{\times}6$, 6^3 is $6{\times}6{\times}6$, 6^2 is $6{\times}6$, and $6^1 = 6$, try to justify in your own words why $6^0 = 1$. Think about the identity property of multiplication and how this might play into your justification.

Examples
Simplify each expression.

3a. 10^0 b. $x^0 \cdot x^3$ c. $(-6)^0$

Quotient Rule for Exponents
When dividing two exponential terms, the bases are matched and the exponents are subtracted.

Use the example $\frac{m^4}{m^3}$ and show why the quotient rule works by both expanding the exponents and also by applying the quotient rule. Are the answers the same?

The order in which you subtract the exponents determines the location of the answer. Top−bottom, the answer goes in the top. Bottom−top, the answer goes in the bottom.

Examples
Simplify each expression.

4a. $\frac{x^6}{x}$ b. $\frac{y^8}{y^2}$ c. $\frac{x^2}{x^2}$

5a. $\frac{15x^{15}}{3x^3}$ b. $\frac{20x^{10}y^6}{2x^2y^3}$

Quick Quiz

Simplify each exponential expression.

1. $7^4 \cdot 7^2$
2. $\frac{9^5}{9^2}$
3. $3x^0 + 9y^0$
4. $(3x^5)(4x^7)$
5. $\frac{28a^6}{14a^2}$

Negative Exponents

If a positive exponent indicates repeated multiplication, what then would a negative exponent indicate?

Write 4^3 as repeated multiplication. Write 4^{-3} as repeated division using one fraction.

How do you rewrite a term with a **negative exponent** as one with a positive exponent?

If the term has multiple variables, some with positive exponents and some with negative, how do you rewrite the term with all positive exponents?

Examples

Rewrite using only positive exponents.

1a. 5^{-1}

b. x^{-3}

c. $x^{-9} \cdot x^7$

Simplify.

2a. $2^{-5} \cdot 2^8$

b. $\frac{x^6}{x^{-1}}$

c. $\frac{10^{-5}}{10^{-2}}$

d. $\frac{x^6y^3}{x^2y^5}$

e. $\frac{15x^{10} \cdot 2x^2}{3x^{15}}$

Quick Quiz

Simplify each exponential expression completely. Make sure all exponents are positive.

1. $-5(x^{-2})$

2. $y^0 \cdot y^6 \cdot y^{-3}$

3. $(3x^5)(4x^{-7})$

4. $(-6a^3b^4)(4a^{-2}b^8)$

5. $-4x^{-3}$

6. $\frac{6a^2b^8}{15a^4b^3}$

Power Rules for Exponents

The power rule refers to an exponential term being raised to another exponent. Sometimes we refer to this as a power^{power} or a "power to a power." The product and quotient rules still apply.

Summarize the rules from previous lessons.

1. Product Rule
2. Quotient Rule
3. Negative Exponent
4. Zero Power

Power Rule for Exponents

When raising an exponential term to a power, the exponents for each base are multiplied by the outer exponent. Coefficients are raised to the power using the basic concept of repeated multiplication.

Use the example $(m^3)^4$ and show why the power rule works by both expanding the exponents and also by applying the power rule. Are the answers the same?

Examples

Simplify. After applying the power rule, write all answers with positive exponents only.

1a. $(x^2)^4$ b. $(x^5)^{-2}$ c. $(y^{-7})^2$ d. $(2^3)^{-2}$

When we raise a complex term to a power, we raise the coefficient to the outer power by repeated multiplication and for each base multiply the exponents.

Illustrate this rule using this example: $(-2x^2y)^5 =$

Concept Check: $(4x^2)^3 =$

Examples

Simplify. After applying the power rule, write all answers with positive exponents only.

2a. $(5x)^2$ b. $(xy)^3$ c. $(-7ab)^2$

d. $(ab)^{-5}$ e. $(x^2y^{-3})^4$

The rules for exponents can be applied to numerical bases as long as each of the bases are treated as a base. Consider the problem $5^3 \cdot 5^2$. Find the value of this expression by following order of operations. Then repeat the problem applying the correct exponential rules learned above. Are the answers the same?

Take caution when working with negative numbers and exponents.
Explain the difference between

-7^2 and $(-7)^2$ $\qquad$ -2^0 and $(-2)^0$

Make a statement that summarizes the relationship between negative coefficients and a power.

When we raise a complex quotient to a power, we can apply the rules to both the numerator and the denominator separately and then simplify. So in each, raise the coefficient to the outer power by repeated multiplication and for each base multiply the exponents.

Illustrate this rule using this example: $\left(\frac{2}{x}\right)^3$

Examples

Simplify. After applying the power rule, write all answers with positive exponents only.

3a. $\left(\frac{y}{x}\right)^5$ $\qquad$ b. $\left(\frac{3}{4}\right)^3$ $\qquad$ c. $\left(\frac{2}{a}\right)^4$ $\qquad$ d. $\left(\frac{x}{7}\right)^2$

When a quotient has common bases in both the numerator and the denominator, what would happen if you followed order of operations and simplified inside the ( ) first versus applying the power rule to eliminate the ( )? Try both methods for the expression $\left(\frac{4x}{x^3}\right)^3$. You can also verify by applying repeated multiplication to the whole expression.

Summarize your findings regarding the order in which exponential expressions can be simplified.

If the outer exponent is a negative, one option is to apply the negative by taking the reciprocal of the fraction in ( ). $\left(\frac{x}{y}\right)^{-1} = \left(\frac{y}{x}\right)^{1}$

Examples

4a. $\left(\frac{-2x}{y^2}\right)^3$

b. $\left(\frac{3a^2b}{a^3b^2}\right)^2$ (show both methods)

Apply power rule first. | Simplify in ( ) first.

5a. $\left(\frac{x^3}{y^5}\right)^{-4}$ (use idea of reciprocals)

b. $\left(\frac{x^3}{y^5}\right)^{-4}$ (apply power rule first)

Many times in math, there are several ways to get to the correct answer. In example 6, show a **different sequence of steps** than provided to get the correct answer.

6. $\left(\frac{2x^2y^3}{3xy^{-2}}\right)^{-2} \left(\frac{4x^2y^{-1}}{3x^{-5}y^3}\right)^{-1}$

Summarize the Rules of Exponents

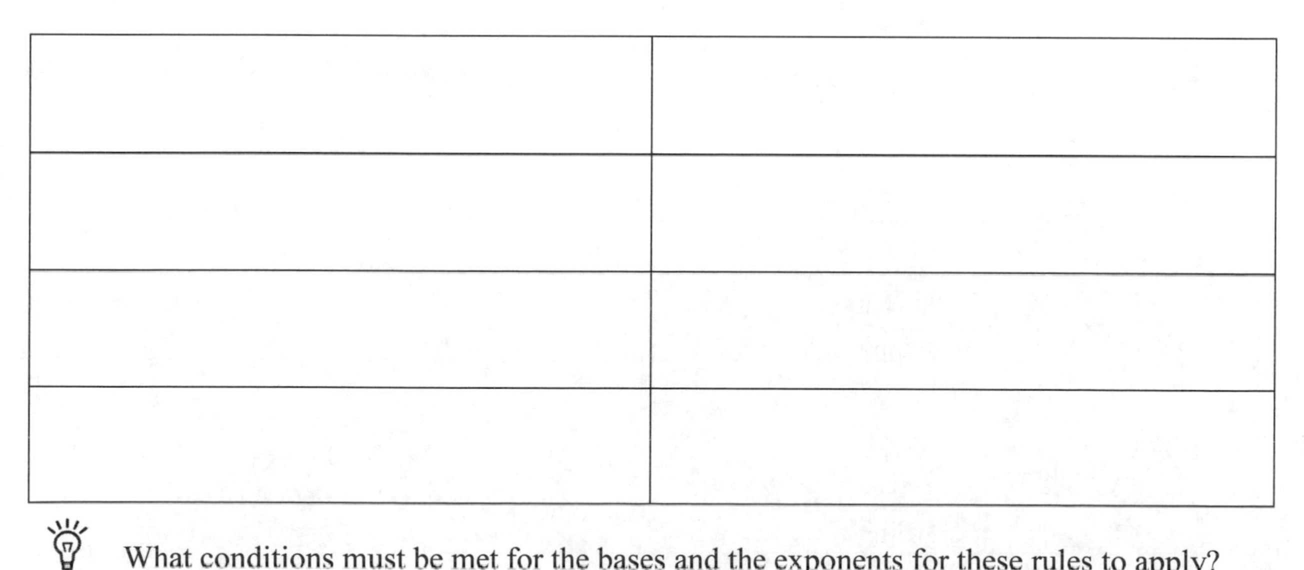

What conditions must be met for the bases and the exponents for these rules to apply?

Quick Quiz

Simplify the exponential expressions completely. Make sure all exponents are positive.

1. $(6x^3)^2$
2. $-4(5x^{-3}y)^{-1}$
3. $\left(\frac{x}{y}\right)^{-2}$
4. $\left(\frac{5xy^3}{y}\right)^2$
5. $\frac{(7x^{-2}y)^2}{(xy^{-1})^2}$
6. $\frac{(5x^2)(3x^{-1})^2}{(25y^3)(6y^{-2})}$

Scientific Notation

Define **scientific notation**.

What is scientific notation used for?

List some areas of study or careers that would use scientific notation on a regular basis.

Answers written in scientific notation should always be between the number 1.0 and 9.99… When a value does not meet that standard, adjustments need to be made.

Examples

Write each decimal number in scientific notation.

1a. 8,720,000 b. 0.000000376

Write each number in scientific notation and then use the properties of exponents to simplify.

2a. $\frac{(0.085)(41{,}000)}{0.00017}$ b. $\frac{(11{,}100)(0.064)}{(8{,}000{,}000)(370)}$

c. Light travels approximately 3×10^8 meters **per second**. How many meters **per minute** does light travel?

Given 35.457×10^5, first the 35.457 needs to be adjusted to 3.5457 but now the power needs adjusting. What should the new power be for $3.5457 \times 10^{?}$? Justify or explain your answer. Check yourself by turning both into a standard number.

Quick Quiz

Perform each operation. Express the answer in scientific notation.

1. $3 \times 10^{12} \cdot 1.5 \times 10^{-5}$

2. $1.25 \times 10^{-8} \div 5 \times 10^9$

Introduction to Polynomials

Terms in a polynomial are separated by addition or subtraction signs.
Factors are separated by multiplication signs.

A polynomial with only one term is called a ____________________________.

A polynomial with two terms is called a ________________________.

A polynomial with three terms is called a ________________________.

A polynomial with more than three terms is called a __________________.

Give some examples of terms that would **NOT** be considered terms in a polynomial:

$\frac{1}{x}$, ________, ________, ________,

These include exponents that are ________________________ or ____________________________.

Why is $\frac{1}{x}$ in the list of NOT terms if x has an understood power of 1?

How do we determine the **degree** of a polynomial?

How do we determine the **leading coefficient** of a polynomial?

These are really important concepts for future work because the degree will indicate the maximum number of solutions in an equation. If your term has multiple variables, the degree of the term is found by adding all the exponents of the term. The leading coefficient of a polynomial can help determine the graph's direction.

Examples
Complete the table.

	Polynomial	Simplify in Descending Order	Degree	Leading Coefficient	Type of Polynomial
1a.	$5x^3 + 7x^3$				
b.	$5x^3 + 7x^3 - 2x$				
c.	$\frac{1}{2}y + 3y - \frac{2}{3}y^2 - 7$				

	Polynomial	Simplify in Descending Order	Degree	Leading Coefficient	Type of Polynomial
d.	$x^2 + 8x - 15 - x^2$				
e.	$-3y^4 + 2y^2 + y^{-1}$				
2.	$x^2 + 7x - 3x + 6 - 3x^2$				

We read "$p(5) =$ " as the function value when x=5. To evaluate $p(5) =$, we substitute 5 for x and simplify. The result is the function value that also satisfies the ordered pair $(x, p(x))$.

Examples

Evaluate.

3a. $p(x) = 4x^2 + 5x - 15$, find $p(3)$ b. $p(y) = 5y^3 + y^2 - 3y + 8$, find $p(-2)$

4. $p(x) = 5x^2 + 6x - 10$, find $p(3)$

Each of the examples above represents a function. For each one, list the independent variable upon which the function depends.

Quick Quiz

Evaluate each polynomial at the given value.

1. Given $p(x) = x^2 - 4x + 13$, find $p(2)$. 2. Given y=3, evaluate $-3y^2 - 15$.

3. Given $p(m) = 2m^4 + 3m^2 - 8m$, find $p(-1)$.

Simplify each polynomial.

4. $y + 3y - 12$ 5. $6x^5 + 2x^4 - 5x^3 - 3x^4$

6. $3x + 7 - x - 1 - 3x$

Addition and Subtraction with Polynomials

When we *combine like terms*, we add or subtract ONLY the coefficients.

What conditions must be met in order for two terms to be declared "like terms"?

Examples

Simplify.

1a. $(5x^3 - 8x^2 + 12x + 13) + (-2x^2 - 8) + (4x^3 - 5x + 14)$

b. $(x^3 - x^2 + 5x) + (4x^3 + 5x^2 - 8x + 9)$

2. $(4x^3 + 15x - 7) + (x^3 - 4x^2 + 6x + 2)$

$-x$ has a coefficient of -1

Show how to distribute: $-(2x^2 + 3x - 7) =$______________________________

Use this information to combine these polynomials: $(5x^2 - 3x - 7) - (2x^2 + 5x - 8)$

Examples

Simplify.

3a. $(9x^4 - 22x^3 + 3x^2 + 10) - (5x^4 - 2x^3 - 5x^2 + x)$

b. $8x^3 + 5x^2 - 14 - (-2x^3 + x^2 + 6x)$

c. Subtract $-11x^3 + x^2 + 4x - 5$ from $4x^4 + 2x^2 - 3x + 5$

The phrase "subtract from" requires some extra thought. Think about 3 from 8.

4. $(6x^3 - 4x^2 + 8x + 14) - (2x^3 - x^2 + 3x - 9)$

Pay attention to the order of operations: PEMDAS

5a. $5x - [2x + 3(4 - x) + 1] - 9$

b. $-3(x - 4) + 2[x + 3(x - 3)]$

Quick Quiz

Simplify each algebraic expression.

1. $-2x^2 - 3x + 9 + (3x^2 - x + 2)$

2. $x^2 - 9x + 2 - (4x^2 - 3x + 4)$

3. $(-4x^2 + 2x + 1) + (2 - x + 3x^2) + (x - 8)$

4. $(x^4 + 8x^3 - 2x^2 - 5) - (11 - 2x^2 + 10x^3)$

Multiplication with Polynomials

Reminders:
Distributive property: $5(2x + 3) =$ ________________
When we multiply two terms with like bases, we ____________ their exponents.
When we combine like terms, we add ONLY the ________________________.

Find the product for these three examples of multiplying polynomials.
Make notes regarding your steps.

A monomial times a polynomial $5x(2x + 3)$	A binomial times a polynomial $(x + 3)(x + 7)$	A trinomial times a polynomial $(2x - 1)(x^2 + x - 5)$

Examples
Find each product.

1a. $-4x(x^2 - 3x + 12)$

b. $(2x - 4)(5x + 3)$

c. $(7y^2 - 3y + 2)(2y + 3)$

d. $(x^2 + 3x - 1)(x^2 - 3x + 1)$

e. $2x(x - 3)(2x + 1)$

f. $(x - 5)(x + 2)(x - 1)$

2a. $3x^2(x^2 + 12x - 5)$

b. $(3x + 8)(5x + 4)$

Quick Quiz

Find each product.

1. $-3x(x - 1)$

2. $(2x^2 + x - 3)(x + 3)$

The FOIL Method

All multiplications of polynomials can be completed by rewriting the terms in the first ( ) so that they are distributed to the second polynomial. However, because we multiply two binomials quite often, having a mental way to do the process can be helpful.

What does **FOIL** stand for? When can it be applied?

In the example below, mark the parts of the product that represent each of the letters in FOIL. Then complete the multiplication applying the FOIL method.

$$(2x + 5)(3x - 7)$$

Examples

Use the FOIL method to find the products.

1a. $(x + 3)(2x + 8)$ b. $(2x - 3)(3x - 5)$ c. $(x + 7)(x - 8)$

2. $(x + 11)(3x - 2)$

Quick Quiz

Find each product.

1. $(x + 2)(5x + 1)$ 2. $(x^2 + 1)(x^2 - 1)$

3. $\left(x + \frac{3}{4}\right)\left(x - \frac{3}{4}\right)$

Special Products of Binomials

Some products of binomials have special characteristics.

Examples

Find the product of each example, watching for a pattern in your answers.

1a. $(x+4)(x-4)$ b. $(3y+7)(3y-7)$ c. $(x^3-6)(x^3+6)$

What similarity do you notice when you compare the products? What are the conditions that caused this – i.e. what is true about the two factors being multiplied?

These factors, such as $(x+4)(x-4)$ are **conjugates** of each other because they are binomial duplicates with the exception of the middle signs being opposite.

Examples

Try to do this problem by applying the concept of conjugates.

2. $(4x+9)(4x-9)$

Why is the product of each example above referred to as a **difference of two squares**?

What creates this result?

Difference of Two Squares
$(x+a)(x-a)=x^2-a^2$

List all the perfect squares up to 400. Work to recall these quickly as well as the base that generated the value.

Which of the following first steps is the correct step for finding $(a+7)^2$? Justify your choice.

OR
Distribute the power: $(a+7)^2=a^2+7^2$
Apply repeated multiplication: $(a+7)^2=(a+7)(a+7)$

Are you sure? Test it by following both first steps to find $(2+7)^2$ and determine if the answers are the same or different and which one is correct.

Remember that the multiplication of two binomials can be completed by applying FOIL or the distribution process. The steps for squaring a binomial is a third way to achieve the same results.

$(x+3)^2$
Find the square using distribution or FOIL.

$(x+3)^2$
Find the square using squares method.

Examples

Square each binomial.

3a. $(2x+3)^2$

b. $(5x-1)^2$

c. $(9-x)^2$

d. $(y^3+1)^2$

e. $4x^2(x+3)^2$

4. $(3x+10)^2$

These are a special case because of the pattern all the answers create. Review your answers. What pattern is created in them?

Perfect Square Trinomials

Square of a Binomial Sum: $(x+a)^2 = x^2 + 2ax + a^2$

Square of a Binomial Difference: $(x-a)^2 = x^2 - 2ax + a^2$

Quick Quiz

Find the product.

1. $(2x+1)(2x-1)$

2. $(3x+0.5)^2$

3. $(2a-b)^2$

Division by a Monomial

Explain how to divide a polynomial by a monomial.

Divide.

$$\frac{4x^3 + 8x^2 - 12x}{4x}$$

Examples

Divide.

1a. $\frac{x^3-6x^2+2x}{3x}$

b. $\frac{15y^4-20y^3+5y^2}{5y^2}$

Can we apply this same concept to a problem where the denominator is a binomial such as $\frac{x^3-6x^2+2x}{3x+5}$? Divide the expression by applying something similar to the method above. To test your theory, pick a number for *x*, plug it into the original problem and into your answer. Did you get the same result? Draw a conclusion.

Quick Quiz

Find the quotient.

1. $\frac{8y^3-16y^2+24y}{8y}$

2. $\frac{110x^4-121x^3+11x^2}{-11x}$

3. $\frac{-56x^4+98x^3-35x^2}{14x^2}$

4. $\frac{20y^5-14y^4+21y^3+42y^2}{4y^2}$

Greatest Common Factor of Two or More Terms

A Prime Number has exactly two factors: one and itself.

What is a **factor**?

What is a **product**?

Give an example and label the factors and the product.

The first step in factoring any polynomial is to identify the Greatest Common Factor (GCF). What does this mean?

Steps to find the GCF of a set of terms.

1.

2.

3.

4. Multiply these factors.

What is the GCF if there is no common prime factor?

Examples

Find the GCF.

1a. $\{30, 45, 75\}$

b. $\{20x^4y,\ 15x^3y,\ 10x^5y^2\}$

Greatest Common Factor of a Polynomial

Factoring Completely

1. **Factor out a GCF** from all terms first. (Make sure to not lose it in the process.)
2.
3. Stay tuned for future steps in factoring process.
4.

How do you factor out the GCF from a polynomial?

If a leading coefficient of a polynomial is negative, we often prefer to **factor out the negative** as part of the GCF.

Examples

Factor each polynomial by factoring out the GCF.

1a. $6n + 30$ b. $x^3 + x$ c. $5x^3 - 15x^2$

d. $2x^4 - 3x^2 + 2$ e. $-4a^5 + 2a^3 - 6a^2$

2a. $4ax^3 + 4ax$ b. $3x^2y^2 - 6xy^2$

c. $-14by^3 - 7b^2y + 21by^2$ d. $13a^4b^5 - 3a^2b^9 - 4a^6b^3$

Quick Quiz

Factor each polynomial by finding the GCF.

1. $11x - 121$ 2. $-2x - 14$

3. $3x^2 - 6x$ 4. $8m^2x^3 - 12m^2y + 4m^2z$

Factoring Expressions by Grouping

Factoring Completely
1. Factor out a GCF from all terms first. (Make sure to not lose it in the process.)
2. Are there four terms? **Factor by Grouping**
3.
4.

Stay tuned for future steps in factoring process.

The Commutative Property of Multiplication says that we can change the order of factors. So $(x+3)(x-1)$ is the same as $(x-1)(x+3)$.

Not all factors have to be a single term. Use the ( ) to identify factors.

(6)(3) 6 and 3 are both factors

$(x+2)(x+3)$ likewise $(x+2)$ and $(x+3)$ are both factors

When looking for common factors, make sure to include any (factor) in your inspection.

Examples

Factor each polynomial.

1a. $3x^2(5x+1)-2(5x+1)$ b. $7a(2x-3)+(2x-3)$

In the following examples, you will be using the Associative Property of Addition which says we are allowed to change the grouping of terms that are added. Remember you can also reorder terms by the Commutative Property of Addition.

Examples

Factor by grouping.

2a. $xy+5x+3y+15$ b. $x^2-xy-5x+5y$ c. $x^2+ax+3x+3y$

d. $xy+5x+y+5$ e. $5xy+6uv-3vy-10ux$

Quick Quiz

Factor each polynomial by grouping.

1. $x^2+x+5x+5$
2. $2z^3-14z^2+3z-21$
3. $2ac-3bc+6ad-9bd$
4. x^2-5+x^2y-5y

Factoring Trinomials with Leading Coefficient 1

Factoring Completely

1. Factor out a GCF from all terms first. (Make sure to not lose it in the process.)
2. Are there four terms? Factor by Grouping
3. Are there three terms?
   Factor by Trial and Error (Un-FOIL) or *ac*-Method (Force Grouping)
4. Stay tuned for future steps in factoring process.

Factoring trinomials can be done several different ways but if a method is mastered it can be applied to all trinomials. Before we learn the specific methods, we will look at the special case of the leading coefficient = 1 to try and factor by observation.

For a trinomial $ax^2 + bx + c$, if $a = 1$, we can factor if we can find two factors of c, whose *sum* is b. If not, the trinomial is said to be **PRIME**.

How can we organize our work so that as the problems get messier we are able to track our progress? Here are a couple of ways to organize the finding of factors that will apply to later methods as well.

If our goal is to find two factors whose product is 30 and whose sum is 11, we can…

<table>
<tr>
<td>Fill in each of the shaded boxes with a number so that across the top they multiply to get 30, and across the bottom they add to get 11.</td>
<td>Create a table so that the first column multiplies the two numbers, the second adds the two numbers to get the values at the top. Stop making the list if you find your pair or if the list starts repeating. Certainly if you know the combo from the beginning, start with that.</td>
<td>Do you have a way you like to organize? Show or describe it below for the same two numbers.</td>
</tr>
<tr>
<td>ac
30
5 * + 6
11
b</td>
<td>
<table>
<tr><th>Product ac (30)</th><th>Sum to b (11)</th></tr>
<tr><td>1·30</td><td>1+30</td></tr>
<tr><td>2·15</td><td>2+15</td></tr>
<tr><td>3·10</td><td>3+10</td></tr>
<tr><td>5·6 = 30</td><td>5+6 = 11</td></tr>
</table>
</td>
<td></td>
</tr>
</table>

Your signs of the numbers are important. Using the organization method of your choice, find the two factors whose product is −18 and whose sum is 3.

Factor each after finding your two numbers that are factors of "*ac*" and whose sum is "*b*".

$x^2 + 8x + 15$
Two numbers:
( )( )

$x^2 + 11x + 30$
Two numbers:
( )( )

Then **FOIL** these factorizations to verify they equal the trinomial.

Examples
Factor each trinomial with Leading Coefficient = 1.

1a. $x^2 + 8x + 12$

b. $y^2 - 8y - 20$

2. $y^2 + 10y + 16$

When we factor a trinomial $ax^2 + bx + c$, we find two factors of *ac* whose sum is *b*.

Why did we just find factors of "*c*" up above when *a*=1 but now we find factors of "*ac*"?

Examples
First factor out the GCF, then factor the remaining trinomial. Make sure your final answer includes all factors needed to reproduce the original polynomial. Show that the factorization is correct by multiplying the factors found.

3a. $5x^3 - 15x^2 + 10x$

b. Verify

3b. $10y^5 - 20y^4 - 80y^3$

b. Verify

Factor and check.

4. $5a^2 + 25a - 180$

What do we call a polynomial that cannot be factored? _______________

Give an example of a trinomial that cannot be factored: ________________________________

Quick Quiz

Factor each trinomial completely.

1. $x^2 - x - 12$

2. $y^2 - 14y + 24$

3. $4x^5 + 28x^4 + 24x^3$

4. $-4p^3 - 36p^2 - 32p$

Factoring Trinomials by Trial and Error

Factoring Completely

1. Factor out a GCF from all terms first. (Make sure to not lose it in the process.)
2. Are there four terms? Factor by Grouping
3. Are there three terms?
   Factor by Trial and Error (Un-FOIL) or *ac*-Method (Force Grouping)
4. Stay tuned for future steps in factoring process.

As you are learning or refreshing on factoring, take the time to learn/try each method. Both methods work all the time. You are encouraged to pick the method most comfortable to you and work consistently with it.

Steps in the **Trial and Error Method**.

1.

2.

3.

Guidelines for the Trial and Error Method regarding signs.

1.

2.

Examples

Factor by using the trial and error method.

1a. $x^2 + 6x + 5$ b. $4x^2 - 4x - 15$ c. $6a^2 - 31a + 5$

Is $(2x + 10)(x + 1)$ factored completely?
Hint: Look at the terms in each factor and review the first rule of factoring: GCF.
Show the complete factorization:

Examples

Factor completely. Remember to check for a GCF first.

2a. $6x^3 - 8x^2 + 2x$

b. $-2x^2 - x + 6$

c. $10x^3 + 5x^2 + 5x$

The next method you will learn takes the "guess work" out of factoring. It takes a minute to learn it, but it is well worth your attention…

Quick Quiz

Factor each trinomial completely.

1. $2x^3 - 3x - 5$

2. $-2y^3 - 3y^2 - y$

3. $12b^2 - 12b + 3$

4. $16x^2 - 8x + 1$

Factoring Trinomials by the *ac*-Method

Factoring Completely

1. Factor out a GCF from all terms first. (Make sure to not lose it in the process.)
2. Are there four terms? Factor by Grouping
3. Are there three terms?
   Factor by Trial and Error (Un-FOIL) or ***ac*-Method (Force Grouping)**
4. Stay tuned for future steps in factoring process.

Use $2x^2 + 9x + 10$ to illustrate the **steps for the *ac*-method**:

$a =$ _______ $b =$ _________ $c =$ ________

	General Method	**Example**
	$ax^2 + bx + c$	$2x^2 + 9x + 10$
	Factor out the GCF if there is one.	
Step 1	Multiply: $a \cdot c$ and identify b.	
Step 2	Find the two integers whose product is ac and whose sum is b. Use your preferred method from lesson 6.9.	
Step 3	Rewrite the polynomial splitting the middle term into 2 terms using the two numbers found in Step 2 as coefficients.	
Step 4	Factor by grouping.	
Step 5	Factor out the common binomial factor.	
Check	Check each factor to confirm no GCF remains. Multiply the factors to check.	

Examples

Factor each trinomial using the *ac*-method.

1a. $3x^2 + 19x + 6$ b. $12y^3 - 26y^2 + 12y$ c. $4x^2 - 5x - 6$

Tips to keep in mind while factoring:

1.

2.

3.

4.

Examples

Factor completely and verify your solution.

2a. $15x^2 + 38x + 7$ b. $15x^2 + 38x + 7$

Quick Quiz

Factor each trinomial completely.

1. $2x^3 - 3x - 5$
2. $-2y^3 - 3y^2 - y$
3. $12b^2 - 12b + 3$
4. $16x^2 - 8x + 1$

Special Factorizations - Squares

Factoring Completely
1. Factor out a GCF from all terms first. (Make sure to not lose it in the process.)
2. Are there four terms? Factor by Grouping
3. Are there three terms? Factor by Trial and Error (Un-FOIL), *ac*-Method (Force Grouping), **or Special Cases**
4. Are there two terms? **Factor Difference of Squares** or Sum/Difference of Cubes

As mentioned earlier, all trinomials can be factored using your preferred method. Below are some special cases that by recognizing them as such you may be able to factor more quickly or identify the pair of numbers more easily.

I Difference of Squares $x^2 - a^2 = (x+a)(x-a)$	II Factoring a perfect square trinomial leads to the square of a binomial sum $x^2 + 2ax + a^2 = (x+a)^2$	III Factoring a perfect square trinomial leads to the square of a binomial difference $x^2 - 2ax + a^2 = (x-a)^2$
Conditions: 1. Two terms. 2. Coefficients are perfect squares. 3. Variables have even powers. 4. Two terms are subtracted.	Conditions: 1. Trinomial 2. First term = $1x^2$ 3. Last term is a perfect square. 4. Middle term = $2ax$ 5. All terms positive.	Conditions: 1. Trinomial 2. First term = $1x^2$ 3. Last term is a perfect square. 4. Middle term = $2ax$ 5. Middle term negative.

How were the numbers in the examples above determined?
Is $(x+5)(x-5)$ the same solution as $(x-5)(x+5)$? Why?

Examples
Factor if possible. If not explain why.

1a. $3a^2b - 3b$ b. $x^6 - 400$ 2a. $y^2 + 64$ b. $4x^2 + 100$

3a. $z^2 - 12z + 36$ b. $4y^2 + 12y + 9$ c. $2x^3 - 8x^2y + 8xy^2$

Here's a fun challenge. To factor this you have to combine the methods. Challenge yourself before you consult the Learn.

3d. $(x^2 + 6x + 9) - y^2$

Quick Quiz

Factor completely.

1. $x^2 - 49$

2. $z^2 + 18z + 81$

3. $x^4 - 16$

4. $x^2 + 64y^2$

Special Factorizations - Cubes

Factoring Completely
1. Factor out a GCF from all terms first. (Make sure to not lose it in the process.)
2. Are there four terms? Factor by Grouping
3. Are there three terms? Factor by Trial and Error (Un-FOIL), *ac*-Method (Force Grouping), or Special Cases
4. Are there two terms? Factor Difference of Squares or **Sum/Difference of Cubes**

Make a list of perfect cubes created when the numbers 1-10 are cubed. Work to be able to recognize these numbers and identify the base that generates each.

Sum of Cubes	**Difference of Cubes**
$x^3 + a^3 = (x + a)(x^2 - ax + a^2)$	$x^3 - a^3 = (x - a)(x^2 + ax + a^2)$
Conditions:	Conditions:
1. Two terms.	1. Two terms.
2. Coefficients are perfect cubes.	2. Coefficients are perfect cubes.
3. Variables have powers divisible by 3.	3. Variables have powers divisible by 3.
4. Two terms are **added**.	4. Two terms are **subtracted**.

Compare the two formulas. What is the only difference between them?
Try writing a general description about the formula that may help you remember them.

Use the appropriate formula to factor, showing steps as you complete the problem.

$x^3 + 27$ $\qquad$ $x^6 - 125$

Examples

Factor completely.

1a. $x^3 - 8$ $\qquad$ b. $x^6 + 64y^3$ $\qquad$ c. $16y^{12} - 250$

Quick Quiz

Factor completely.

1. $x^3 - 64$ $\qquad$ 2. $8x^6 - 27$

Additional Factoring Practice

Factoring Completely

1. Factor out a GCF from all terms first. (Make sure to not lose it in the process.)
2. Are there four terms? Factor by Grouping
3. Are there three terms? Factor by Trial and Error (Un-FOIL), *ac*-Method (Force Grouping), or Special Cases
4. Are there two terms? Factor Difference of Squares or Sum/Difference of Cubes

Always check to make sure your final factors do not have a GCF remaining in them.
Check your work by multiplying the factors together to get the original polynomial.

In order to make sure you have factored completely you should repeatedly ask the following questions until the answer is no. Then move to the next question.

1. Is there a GCF? If so, pull it out.
2. Are there four terms? If so, can you factor them by grouping?
3. Are there three terms? If so, can you factor them by your preferred method?
4. Are there two terms? If so, are they factorable by the difference of squares or sum/difference of cubes?

Make additional notes here to create a reference page for all of your factoring methods.

Quick Quiz

Factor completely.

1. $x^2 + 11x + 18$
2. $-x^2 - 12x - 35$
3. $x^2 + 3x - 10$
4. $6x^2 - 11x + 4$
5. $6t^2 + t - 35$
6. $x^3 + 125$
7. $9y^2 + 24y + 16$
8. $16x^3 - 100x$

Solving Quadratic Equations by Factoring

Define **quadratic equations**.

Define **zero-factor property**.

If you have two numbers whose product is 0, what has to be true about one of the numbers? So if you have two factors of a quadratic =0, what has to be true about one of the factors?

Summarize the steps demonstrated throughout the lesson for solving a quadratic equation by factoring.

What is the degree of a quadratic equation? How many solutions can a quadratic equation have? (The degree of the equation indicates the maximum solutions possible.)

Examples

Solve the quadratic equation. Check your solution(s) by substituting into the original.

1. $(x-5)(2x-7)=0$

2a. $3x^2 = 6x$

b. $x^2 - 8x + 16 = 0$

2c. $4x^2 - 4x = 24$

d. $(x+5)^2 = 36$

e. $3x(x-1) = 2(5-x)$

f. $\frac{2x^2}{15} - \frac{x}{3} = -\frac{1}{5}$

Hint: consider eliminating fractions first.

What is a **double root**?

Which example above produced a double root?

This is another important concept for your future. It tells us something special about the graph of the function.

3. $(x-2)^2 = 64$

4. $2x^3 - 4x^2 - 6x = 0$

Create an equation given the factors or solutions to that equation.
Equations are often created by knowing their solutions and working backwards.

Given the roots (solutions) to the equation.	**Given that $x = 5$ and $x = -2$ are roots (solutions) to the equation**
Write them as factors, equation = 0.	$x = 5$ is $x - 5 = 0$ $x = -2$ is $x + 2 = 0$
The factors have a product of 0.	$(x - 5)(x + 2) = 0$
Find the product to create the equation.	$x^2 - 3x - 10 = 0$

Quick Quiz

Solve each quadratic equation by factoring.

1. $x^2 - 3x - 4 = 0$

2. $4x^2 - 12x + 9 = 0$

3. $x^2 = x + 30$

4. $9x^2 = 36$

Applications of Quadratic Equations

Strategies for application problems:

1.

2.

3.

4.

5.

6.

What are some personal strategies you use when solving applications?

Examples

1a. One number is four more than another and the sum of their squares is 296. What are the numbers?

b. In an orange grove, there are 10 more trees in each row than there are rows. How many rows are there if there are 96 trees in the grove?

c. The width of a rectangle is 11 feet less than the length. If the area is 60 square feet, find the length and width of the rectangle.

d. A man wants to build a fence on three sides of a rectangular-shaped lot he owns. If 180 feet of fencing is needed and the area of the lot is 4000 square feet, what are the dimensions of the lot?

Describe the algebraic relationship between the following integer relationships.

Consecutive Integers	Consecutive Even Integers	Consecutive Odd Integers

Why do we use even numbers to represent odd numbers?

Examples

2a. Find two consecutive **positive** integers such that the sum of their squares is 265.

b. Find three consecutive odd integers such that the product of the first and the second is 68 more than the third.

Pythagorean Theorem
$\boldsymbol{a^2 + b^2 = c^2}$

What relationship is the Pythagorean Theorem describing? What do *a*, *b*, and *c* stand for?

Examples

3. A support wire is 25 feet long and stretches from a tree to a point on the ground. The point of attachment on the tree is 5 feet higher than the distance from the base of the tree to the point of attachment on the ground. How far up the tree is the point of attachment?

   1. Draw a picture.
   2. Label the pieces you know.
   3. Use a formula to find the unknown.
   4. Re-read the question and answer using the information gained.

Quick Quiz

1. A support wire is attached x feet from the top of a 17-foot pole to protect the pole during a blizzard. The other end of each wire is attached to a stake x feet from the base of the pole. The wire used is 13 feet long. Draw a sketch to represent this application, solve for x, and interpret your solutions.

2. A family wants to fence in a rectangular area of their yard next to the house so their dog can play outside without being on a leash. One side of the fenced-in area will be along the side of the house, so they will only need to fence in three sides. The family decides to fence in an area of 4000 square feet and they purchase 180 feet of fencing. What are the dimensions of the fenced-in area? Is there more than one option? If so which is better and why?

Vocabulary Check

Define each of the following terms in your own words, providing examples as necessary to clarify the term.

Base

Binomial

Degree

Exponent

Factor

GCF

LCM

Leading Coefficient

Like Terms

Monomial

Numerical Coefficient

Polynomial

Term

Trinomial

Concept Review

Answer the following questions as completely as possible in your own words. Make sure to get the big points of each with key steps involved.

1. What is anything^0 ?

2. What does a negative power indicate? How can you force the power to become positive?

3. When terms contain powers, what do you do when…
(address what to do with the coefficients and what to do with powers)
Terms are added or subtracted?
Terms are multiplied?
Terms are divided?
Terms are raised to a power?

4. How do you identify polynomials as:
   Monomials Binomials Trinomials

5. What are the steps in adding or subtracting monomials, binomials, or trinomials?

6. If you have a polynomial × polynomial, how do you multiply the two?

7. If you have a polynomial ÷ monomial, how do you divide?

8. How do you convert between standard notation and scientific notation?

9. When using power rules and the base is a number, how do you deal with the base?

10. What are the four major steps in factoring?

11. How do you factor out a GCF?

12. How do you factor a polynomial with four terms?

13. How do you factor a trinomial of the form $x^2 + bx + c$ or $ax^2 + bx + c$?

14. How do you factor a binomial? What conditions must be met?

15. What does it mean to factor completely?

16. How do you factor a difference of squares?

17. How do you factor a sum of two cubes?

18. How do you factor a difference of two cubes?

19. How do you solve an equation with degree 2 or greater?

20. What is the degree of an equation and what does it tell us?

Unit 7

Rational Expressions and Equations

Introduction to Rational Expressions

Define **rational expressions.**

What makes a fraction undefined?

$\frac{0}{5} =$ ________ $\frac{5}{0} =$ ________ $\frac{0}{0} =$ ________

What are **restrictions on a domain**?

How do you identify the restrictions?

Examples

1. Find the restrictions (if there are any) for each rational expression.

a. $\frac{5}{3x-1}$ b. $\frac{x^2-4}{x^2-5x-6}$ c. $\frac{x+3}{x^2+36}$

2. Evaluate each rational expression for the given value of the variable.

a. $\frac{2x}{x^2+1}$ for $x = 2$ b. $\frac{a-3}{a^2-5}$ for $a = 3$

Why is it important to use parentheses for the values we substitute?

Take a moment to review operations with fractions – these concepts apply to rational expressions as well. Special attention to the reminders below.

Adding and Subtracting	Multiplying	Dividing
Requires a common denominator. Reducing across + or – signs cannot occur.	Factors in both the numerator and denominator can be reduced. (Divide-out/Cancel)	Dividing by a fraction – multiply by the reciprocal.

How do you **simplify a rational expression?**

Examples

Simplify each rational expression and state any restrictions. Remember that factoring out a −1 manipulates the signs of the terms.

3a. $\frac{2x-10}{3x-15}$ b. $\frac{x^3-64}{x^2-16}$ c. $\frac{y-10}{10-y}$

Why is it possible to cancel common factors when one is in the numerator and the other is in the denominator?

We **CAN reduce (cancel) factors of monomials.**
Example $\frac{2x}{3x}$ would reduce to $\frac{2}{3}$ *by canceling the x's.*

But we can **NOT reduce (cancel) terms of binomials.**
Show how to correctly simplify $\frac{4x+8}{8}$ $\frac{x^2-9}{x-3}$

Summarize the **rules for exponents.**

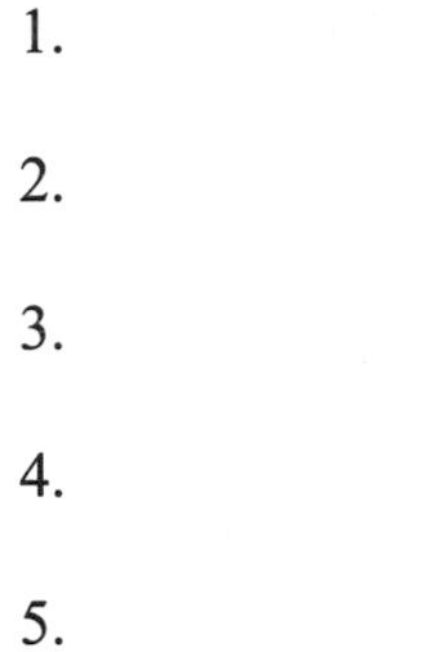

1.

2.

3.

4.

5.

Examples

4. Use the basic rules for exponents to simplify each expression with positive powers only.

a. $x^{-5}y^3z^{-2}$ b. $\frac{x^4y^{-6}}{xx^2}$ c. $\frac{(x^2-4)(x-2)^2}{(x+2)^{-1}}$

Quick Quiz

1. Find any restrictions. $\frac{-3}{3x-8}$

2. Simplify. $\frac{3(x-5)}{5-x}$

3. Simplify. $\frac{x^2+x-20}{x^2+3x-10}$

4. Simplify. $\frac{2x^3y^2}{4x^2y}$

Multiplication and Division with Rational Expressions

Steps to multiply rational expressions.

1.

2.

3.

Multiply. $\frac{2x}{x-6} \cdot \frac{x+5}{x-4}$ $\frac{y^2-4}{y^3} \cdot \frac{y^2-3y}{y^2-y-6}$

Examples

Multiply, reduce, and list any restrictions.

3a. $\frac{5x^2y}{9xy^3} \cdot \frac{6x^3y^2}{15xy^4}$

b. $\frac{x}{x-2} \cdot \frac{x^2-4}{x^2}$

c. $\frac{3x-3}{x^2+x} \cdot \frac{x^2+2x+1}{3x^2-6x+3}$

d. $\frac{x^2-7x+12}{2x+6} \cdot \frac{x^2-4}{x^2-2x-8}$

Generally, we leave the **denominator factored** but the **numerator multiplied out**. This will make future math steps easier. Make sure to check to see if the numerator can be factored and the expression reduced.

4. $\frac{x^2-36}{x^4} \cdot \frac{x}{x-6}$

Why can't we cancel two common factors that are both in the numerator?

To divide rational expressions, multiply by the reciprocal.

Examples

Divide each and simplify.

5a. $\frac{12x^2y}{10xy^2} \div \frac{3x^4y}{xy^3}$

b. $\frac{x^2-y^2}{x^3} \div \frac{y-x}{xy}$

c. $\frac{x^2-8x+15}{2x^2+11x+5} \div \frac{2x^2-5x-3}{4x^2-1}$

6. $\frac{x^2-4}{2x-1} \div \frac{x^2-2x}{2x^2+x-1}$

Quick Quiz

Multiply or Divide each and simplify.

1. $\frac{5y}{4(x^2-16)} \cdot \frac{x(4-x)}{10y}$

2. $\frac{x^2+9x+20}{y(x+5)} \cdot \frac{y}{x+4}$

3. $\frac{4x^2+5x-6}{x} \div \frac{x^2+5x+6}{xy}$

4. $\frac{3x}{4(y^2-9)} \div \frac{2x}{3y-y^2}$

Addition and Subtraction with Rational Expressions

Recall the steps for adding and subtracting fractions.

$$\frac{2}{3} = \frac{10}{15}$$

$$+\ \frac{4}{5} = \frac{12}{15}$$

$$\frac{22}{15}$$

1. Find the common denominator.
2. Create equivalent fractions with common denominators.
   "*Whatever you did to the bottom, you have to do to the top.*"
3. Add or subtract the numerators, keep the denominator.
4. Reduce if possible.

For adding and subtracting fractions, these steps remain the same with the additional step of stating restrictions that cause the denominator to be zero.

Examples

1a. $\frac{x}{x^2-1} + \frac{1}{x^2-1}$

b. $\frac{1}{x^2+7x+10} + \frac{2x+3}{x^2+7x+10}$

If all factors of an expression in the numerator or denominator reduce (cancel), what numerical value does it have?

How do you find the common denominator of expressions with polynomials in the denominator(s)?

Examples

2a. Find the LCD of $\frac{5x}{x+4}$ and $\frac{2x+1}{3x-1}$. LCD = ____________

b. Find the LCD of $\frac{2x-3}{x^2+6x+8}$ and $\frac{3}{x^2-4}$. LCD = ____________

Once the common denominator is determined, how are the numerators adjusted so that the fractions stay equivalent?

3. Find the numerator so that the rational expressions are equal.

a. $\frac{5}{3x+2} = \frac{}{4x(3x+2)}$

b. $\frac{4x+1}{x^2+6x+9} = \frac{}{(x+3)^2(2x+1)}$

Steps to add or subtract rational expressions.

1.

2.

3.

4

Examples

Add or subtract as indicated. Problems may be worked horizontally or vertically.

4a. $\frac{y}{y-3} + \frac{6}{y+4}$

b. $\frac{1}{x^2+6x+9} + \frac{1}{x^2-9} + \frac{1}{2x+6}$

5. $\frac{y}{y-5} + \frac{3}{y+6}$

As usual, when we deal with subtraction, we must watch those negatives. We can write a negative in different locations to have equivalent fractions.

True	False	False
$-\frac{6}{x+7} = \frac{-6}{x+7}$	$-\frac{x+6}{x+7} = \frac{-x+6}{x+7}$	$-\frac{6}{x+7} = \frac{6}{-x+7}$

Rewrite the two false statements to create true statements. Then describe how to correctly handle the minus or negative sign in front of a fraction.

Examples

Add or subtract and reduce. Problems may be worked horizontally or vertically.

6a. $\frac{2x-5y}{x+y}-\frac{3x-7y}{x+y}$

b. $\frac{x^2}{x^2+4x+4}-\frac{2x+8}{x^2+4x+4}$

c. $\frac{x}{x-5}-\frac{3}{5-x}$

7a. $\frac{x+5}{x-5}-\frac{100}{x^2-25}$

b. $\frac{x+y}{(x-y)^2}-\frac{x}{2x^2-2y^2}$

c. $\frac{3x-12}{x^2+x-20}-\frac{x^2+5x}{x^2+9x+20}$

d. $\frac{x+1}{xy-3y+4x-12}-\frac{x-3}{xy+6y+4x+24}$

8. $\frac{x}{x^2-x-2}-\frac{1}{x-2}$

Quick Quiz

Perform the indicated operation and simplify.

1. $\frac{3x}{x-4}+\frac{4x}{4-x}$

2. $\frac{3x}{x+2}-\frac{x+1}{x+2}$

3. $\frac{5}{5x(x-3)}+\frac{8}{5x(x+3)}$

4. $\frac{5}{x-2}-\frac{7x+3}{x^2+6x-16}$

Complex Fractions

Define **complex fraction.**

Steps to simplify complex fractions. (Method 1: Division)

1.

2.

3.

Examples

Simplify by applying the method of division.

1. $\frac{\frac{3x}{y^2}}{\frac{12x}{7y}}$

2a. $\frac{\frac{1}{x+3}-\frac{1}{x}}{1+\frac{3}{x}}$

b. $\frac{x+y}{x^{-1}+y^{-1}}$

Steps to simplify complex fractions. (Method 2: Clearing fractions)

1.

2.

3.

Examples

Simplify by applying the method of clearing fractions.

3a. $\frac{\frac{1}{x+3}-\frac{1}{x}}{1+\frac{3}{x}}$

b. $\frac{x+y}{x^{-1}+y^{-1}}$

 Which method do you prefer? Why?

4. Simplify. Make sure to follow the order of operations.
$\frac{4-x}{x+3}+\frac{x}{x+3}\div\frac{x}{x-3}$

Quick Quiz

Simplify the complex fractions

1. $\frac{2+\frac{2}{x}}{3-\frac{4}{x^2}}$

2. $\left(\frac{1}{x}+\frac{6}{x+7}\right)\cdot\frac{4x+28}{x+1}$

3. $\frac{1}{2x^{-2}+5y^{-2}}$

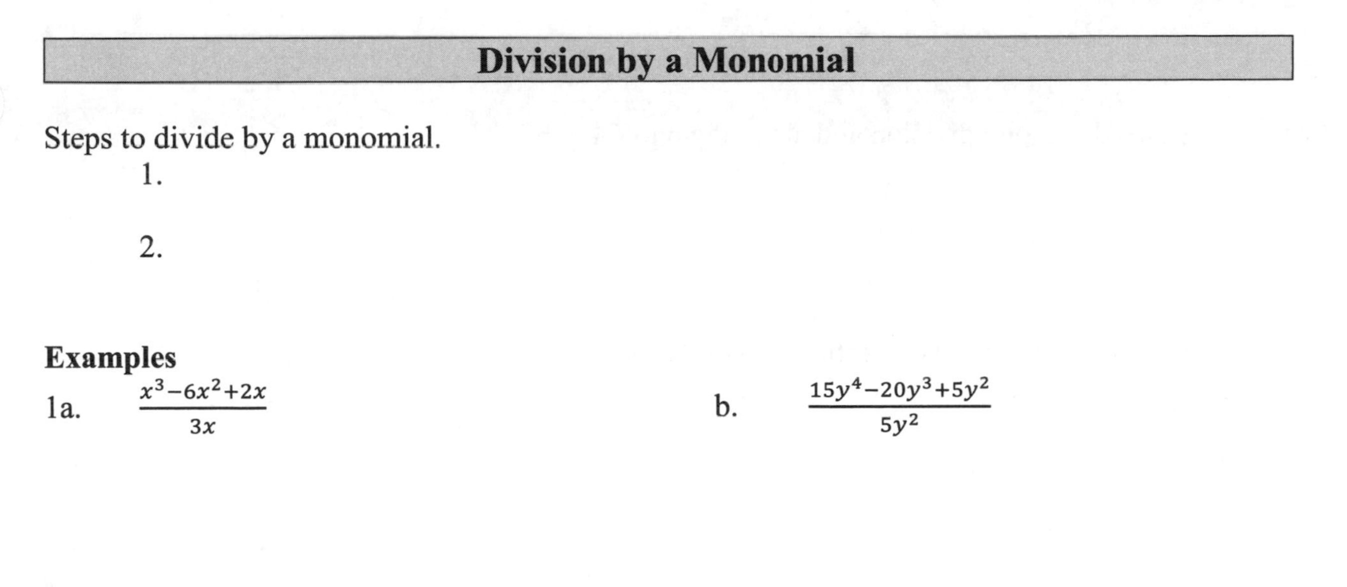

Division by a Monomial

Steps to divide by a monomial.

1.

2.

Examples

1a. $\frac{x^3-6x^2+2x}{3x}$

b. $\frac{15y^4-20y^3+5y^2}{5y^2}$

It is possible for a denominator to end up with a variable.
Create an example where that happens.

Quick Quiz

Divide and simplify your answer.

1. $\frac{8+8a}{2a}$

2. $\frac{4y^5+6y-5}{y}$

3. $\frac{-8y-6}{-2y}$

The Division Algorithm

List the steps used for long division and apply them to $64 \div 5$.

Steps for **dividing polynomials**. (Notice the similarities.)

1.

2.

3.

4.

5.

6.

Examples

1. $(6x^2 - 7x - 2) \div (2x - 1)$

2. $(25x^3 - 5x^2 + 3x + 1) \div (5x + 1)$

3. $(x^4 + 9x^2 - 3x + 5) \div (x^2 - x)$

Why do we need to use a zero as a placeholder in the dividend? What might happen if we didn't?

Quick Quiz

Divide.

1. $(4x^3 - 2x + 1) \div (x - 1)$

2. $\frac{m^2-16}{m-4}$

3. $\frac{n^3-64}{n-4}$

4. $\frac{-8x-6}{-2x}$

5. $\frac{3x+6x^2-8}{1+2x}$

Solving Equations with Rational Expressions

Steps to solve an equation with rational expressions:

#	Step	Show steps here to solve $\frac{3}{x}+\frac{1}{8}=\frac{13}{4x}$.
1	Find the LCD	
2	Multiply both sides of the equation by this LCD and Simplify	
3	Solve the resulting equation	
4	Check each solution in the original equation. Watch out for restricted values.	

What are **restrictions or restricted values**?

How do we find the restricted values?

What are **extraneous solutions**?

How do we determine if a solution is extraneous?

Examples

Solve each equation. Remember to check for any restrictions and extraneous solutions.

1a. $\frac{x-5}{2x}=\frac{6}{3x}$

b. $\frac{1}{x-4}=\frac{3}{x^2-5x}$

Since both examples in number 1 are proportions, would we get the same answers if we solved these using cross-multiplication?

c. $\frac{x}{x-2}+\frac{x-6}{x(x-2)}=\frac{5x}{x-2}-\frac{10}{x-2}$

d. $\frac{2}{x+7}=1+\frac{3}{x-3}$

e. $\frac{2}{x^2-9}=\frac{1}{x^2}+\frac{1}{x^2-3x}$

2. $\frac{x}{x-1}-\frac{3x+1}{x^2+4x-5}=\frac{x+2}{x+5}$

How do you isolate or solve for a variable?

Examples

3. Solve the formula for *h*. $S=2\pi r^2+2\pi rh$

Quick Quiz

1. Solve. $\frac{5x}{4}-\frac{1}{2}=-\frac{3}{16}$

2. Solve the formula for *f*. $w=\frac{f-i}{t}$

3. Solve the formula for *a*. $D=vt+\frac{1}{2}at^2$

4. Set up a proportion and solve: At the horse farm, 6 out of 90 horses are lame. If the number of horses is increased to 3000, how many horses can we expect to be lame?

5. Set up a proportion and solve: In 2013, 1 in 13 adults were considered to be morbidly obese. If approximately 24 million people were morbidly obese, what was the total adult population?

Applications: Rational Expressions

Steps to solve a word problem containing rational expressions

1.

2.

3.

4.

5.

6.

Examples

1. The denominator of a fraction is 8 more than the numerator. If both the numerator and denominator are increased by 3, the new fraction is equal to $\frac{1}{2}$. Find the original fraction.

2a. A carpenter can build a certain type of patio cover in 6 hours. His partner takes 8 hours to build the same cover. How long would it take them working together to build this type of patio cover?

2b. A man can wax his car three times faster than his daughter can. Together they can do the job in 4 hours. How long would it take each of them working alone?

2c. A man was told that his new pool would fill through an inlet valve in 3 hours. He knew something was wrong when the pool took 8 hours to fill. He found he had left the drain valve open. How long would it take to drain the pool once it is completely filled and only the drain valve is open?

3a. On Lake Itasca a man can row his boat 5 miles per hour. On the nearby Mississippi River it takes him the same time to row 5 miles downstream as it does to row 3 miles upstream. What is the speed of the river current in miles per hour?

3b. If a passenger train travels three times as fast as a freight train, and the freight train takes 4 hours longer to travel 210 miles, what is the speed of each train?

What are some reading strategies that could be applied to reading word problems to help in the level of understanding?

Quick Quiz

Solve each application showing all your work.

1. John had \$1248 after he spent $\frac{1}{3}$ of his college budget on books and $\frac{1}{8}$ of his budget on supplies. How much was his total college budget?

2. The ratio of tickets sold to attendees was 12 to 11. If there were 8,000 people present, how many tickets were sold? (Round to the nearest whole number.)

3. One number is $\frac{2}{3}$ of another number. The sum of the two numbers is 150. Find the two numbers.

Vocabulary Check

Define each of the following terms in your own words, providing examples as necessary to clarify the term.

Complex Fraction

Extraneous Roots

Rational Expression

Restricted Values

Concept Review

Answer the following questions as completely as possible in your own words. Make sure to get the big points of each with key steps involved.

1. Write in your own words the Fundamental Principle of Rational Expressions.

2. Explain how to find the opposite of a rational expression.

3. Give a brief explanation of how to perform each operation on rational expressions.

    Addition and Subtraction

    Multiplication

    Division

4. What are the steps to find the least common denominator of rational expressions?

5. How do we divide a polynomial by a monomial?

6. How do we solve an equation with rational expressions?

7. What are some steps or strategies to solve word problems?

8. What are the rules for negative exponents?

9. What makes a rational expression undefined? How do you state the restrictions?

10. What are the steps in performing long division?

11. Why (and when) is it possible to just "cancel" something when it is both in the top and bottom? Clearly identify the necessary conditions.

12. When you add or subtract two fractions, what must you have? How do you get it?

13. Describe the two methods to simplify a complex fraction.

14. When you have a fraction over a fraction, how do you simplify that to make it into an expression with only one numerator and one denominator?

15. Whenever we solve a rational equation, what must you check for before stating your solution? What two things can cause this to happen?

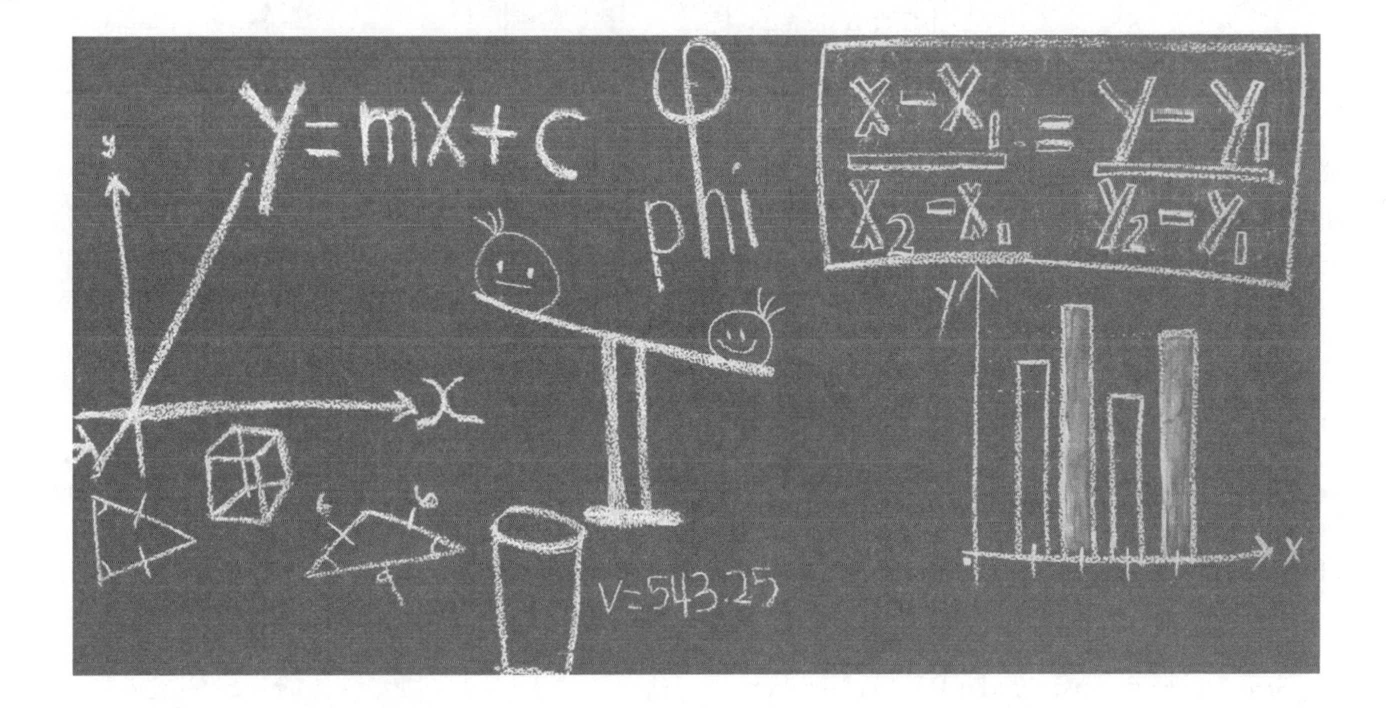

Unit 8

Roots, Radicals, and Complex Numbers

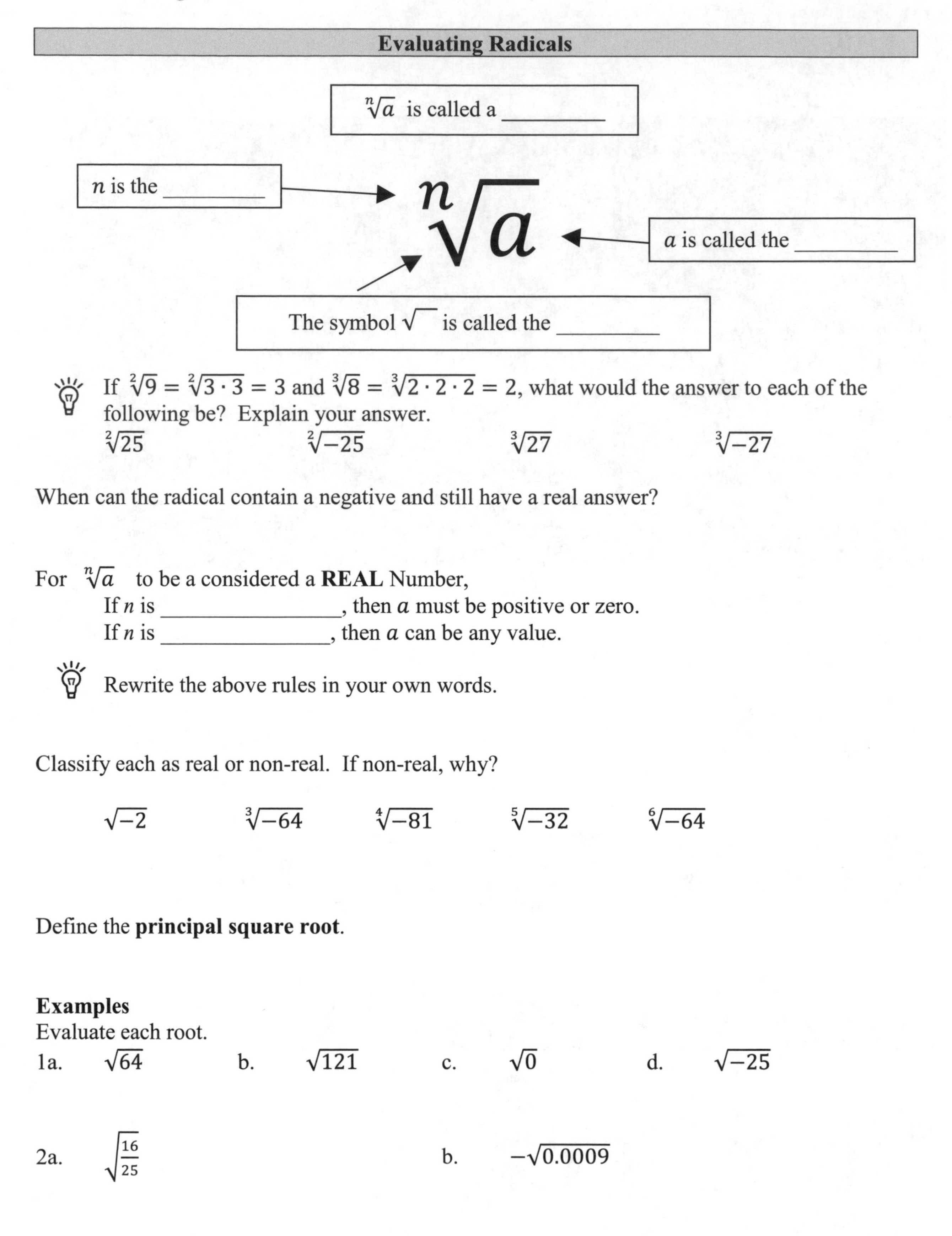

Evaluating Radicals

$\sqrt[n]{a}$ is called a ________

n is the ________

a is called the ________

The symbol $\sqrt{}$ is called the ________

If $\sqrt[2]{9} = \sqrt[2]{3 \cdot 3} = 3$ and $\sqrt[3]{8} = \sqrt[3]{2 \cdot 2 \cdot 2} = 2$, what would the answer to each of the following be? Explain your answer.

$\sqrt[2]{25}$ $\qquad$ $\sqrt[2]{-25}$ $\qquad$ $\sqrt[3]{27}$ $\qquad$ $\sqrt[3]{-27}$

When can the radical contain a negative and still have a real answer?

For $\sqrt[n]{a}$ to be a considered a **REAL** Number,

If n is ________________, then a must be positive or zero.

If n is ________________, then a can be any value.

Rewrite the above rules in your own words.

Classify each as real or non-real. If non-real, why?

$\sqrt{-2}$ $\qquad$ $\sqrt[3]{-64}$ $\qquad$ $\sqrt[4]{-81}$ $\qquad$ $\sqrt[5]{-32}$ $\qquad$ $\sqrt[6]{-64}$

Define the **principal square root**.

Examples

Evaluate each root.

1a. $\sqrt{64}$ $\qquad$ b. $\sqrt{121}$ $\qquad$ c. $\sqrt{0}$ $\qquad$ d. $\sqrt{-25}$

2a. $\sqrt{\frac{16}{25}}$ $\qquad$ b. $-\sqrt{0.0009}$

What is an irrational number and under what conditions would a square root be irrational? Such a root would be an estimate.

3. What two integers is $\sqrt{30}$ between? Use a calculator and round $\sqrt{30}$ to four places.

Why is the cube root of a negative number a negative number?

Evaluate the cube roots.

4a. $\sqrt[3]{8}$ b. $\sqrt[3]{-216}$ c. $\sqrt[3]{\frac{1}{27}}$

Use a calculator to evaluate the radical to the nearest thousandth. Check your answer for reasonableness.

5a. $\sqrt{15}$ b. $3\sqrt{20}$ c. $\sqrt[3]{9}$

Quick Quiz

Identify each number as rational, irrational or non-real.

1. $\sqrt{17}$ 2. $\sqrt[3]{-8}$ 3. $-\sqrt{\frac{1}{4}}$ 4. $\sqrt{-10}$

Simplify. If the result is not a real number, write "not a real number."

5. $\sqrt{36}$ 6. $-\sqrt{100}$ 7. $\sqrt{\frac{25}{81}}$ 8. $\sqrt{-49}$

9. $-\sqrt[3]{\frac{27}{64}}$

Evaluate with a calculator. Round your answer to the nearest thousandth.

10. $\sqrt{39}$ 11. $4\sqrt{5}$ 12. $\sqrt{\frac{1}{5}}$ 13. $-2-\sqrt{12}$

Rational Exponents

Rational exponents and radical expressions can be used to express the same value. It is sometimes more helpful to have an expression written in one form versus the other.

Define the relationship between **radical notation** and **fractional exponents**.

If $\sqrt[4]{16}$ can be written as $16^{\frac{1}{4}}$; then $\sqrt[5]{243}$ can be written as ____________.

Examples

1. Write the exponential form as a radical, then evaluate without a calculator.

	Exponential	Radical	Value
a.	$49^{\frac{1}{2}}$		
b.	$81^{\frac{1}{4}}$		
c.	$(-8)^{\frac{1}{3}}$		
d.	$(0.00001)^{\frac{1}{5}}$		
e.	$(-16)^{\frac{1}{2}}$		

Recall some rules for exponents and **give your own an example** to illustrate each.

Rule	Example
1. Exponent of 1: $a^1 =$ ________.	
2. Exponent of 0: 0^0 is undefined, but if $a \neq 0$, then $a^0=$ __________.	
3. Product rule: When multiplying bases, exponents are ___________.	
4. Quotient rule: When dividing bases, exponents are _______________.	
5. Negative exponents: When a base is moved between numerator and denominator, the __________ of the exponent changes.	
6. Power rule: When raising a power to another power, exponents are __________________.	

7. Power of a product: If a product is raised to a power, each factor can be raised to the same ___________.	
8. Power of a quotient: If a fraction is raised to a power, the numerator and denominator can be raised to the same ___________.	

Define the **general form** $a^{\frac{m}{n}}$ using rational exponents and radical notation.

Examples

2. Rewrite each expression in its other form:

	Exponential	Radical
a.	$x^{\frac{2}{3}}$	
b.	$3x^{\frac{4}{5}}$	
c.	$-a^{\frac{3}{2}}$	
d.		$\sqrt[6]{a^5}$
e.		$5\sqrt{x}$
f.		$-\sqrt[3]{4}$

Expressions using rational exponents can be simplified using the rules for exponents.

Examples

Simplify each expression:

3a. $x^{\frac{2}{3}} \cdot x^{\frac{1}{6}}$ b. $\dfrac{x^{\frac{3}{4}}}{x^{\frac{1}{3}}}$ c. $\left(2a^{\frac{1}{4}}\right)^3$ d. $\left(27y^{-\frac{9}{10}}\right)^{-\frac{1}{3}}$

e. $(36)^{-\frac{1}{2}}$ f. $9^{\frac{2}{4}}$ g. $\left(\dfrac{49x^6y^{-2}}{z^{-4}}\right)^{\frac{1}{2}}$

Change each radical expression into exponential form, then simplify and return it back into radical form.

4a. $\sqrt[4]{\sqrt[3]{x}}$

b. $\sqrt[3]{a\sqrt{a}}$

c. $\frac{\sqrt{x^3}\ \sqrt[3]{x^2}}{\sqrt[5]{x^2}}$

Quick Quiz

Convert each expression into radical notation.

1. $x^{\frac{3}{4}}$

2. $(25x)^{\frac{5}{2}}$

3. $-16a^{\frac{5}{4}}$

Convert each expression into exponential notation.

4. $\sqrt[5]{a}$

5. $\sqrt[3]{8x^2}$

6. $(\sqrt[5]{x})^2$

Simplify.

7. $\left(2x^{\frac{1}{3}}\right)^3$

8. $\frac{a^{\frac{2}{3}}}{a^{\frac{1}{9}}}$

9. $\frac{x^{\frac{2}{3}} \cdot x^{\frac{4}{3}}}{x^2}$

11. $(-x^3y^6z^{-6})^{\frac{2}{3}}$

Simplifying Radicals

Properties of nth Roots: If a and b are positive real numbers, then…

1. Ex. $\sqrt{144} = \sqrt{36} \cdot \sqrt{4}$

2. Ex. $\sqrt{\frac{49}{36}} = \frac{\sqrt{49}}{\sqrt{36}}$

We can use these properties (in both directions) to manipulate radicals to make simplifying easier.

When is the square root considered to be in simplest form?

Simplifying a radical can be approached two different way.

Identifying Perfect Factors	$\sqrt{200} = \sqrt{2 \cdot 100} = \sqrt{2} \cdot \sqrt{100} = \sqrt{2} \cdot 10 = 10\sqrt{2}$
Identifying Prime Factors	$\sqrt{200} = \sqrt{2 \cdot 2 \cdot 2 \cdot 5 \cdot 5} = \sqrt{2 \cdot 2} \cdot \sqrt{5 \cdot 5} \cdot \sqrt{2} = 2 \cdot 5 \cdot \sqrt{2} = 10\sqrt{2}$

Examples

Simplify.

1a. $\sqrt{48}$ b. $\sqrt{63}$ c. $\sqrt{\frac{75}{16}}$

Under what conditions does the expression $\sqrt{x^2} = x$ and when does the expression $\sqrt{x^2} = |x|$? Work to explain your answers in your own words.

Examples

Simplify.

2a. $\sqrt{16y^2}$ b. $\sqrt{72a^2}$ c. $\sqrt{12x^2y^2}$

How do you determine the square root of terms with exponents?

How could the concepts of division and its remainder be used to find the root?

Examples
Simplify.

3a. $\sqrt{81x^4}$ b. $\sqrt{64x^5y}$ c. $\sqrt{18a^4b^6}$ d. $\sqrt{\frac{9a^{13}}{b^4}}$

Why must it be assumed that all of the variables in example 3 represent positive real numbers?

Notice in all of the examples so far, we have been looking at radicals with the index of 2. The **index of 2** determines that we need a **perfect square** to "come out" of the radical. Now we will look at examples that have an **index of 3**. This means that we need a **perfect cube** to "come out" of the radical.

How do you determine the cube root of terms with exponents?

How could the concepts of division and its remainder be used to find the root?

Show why each radical has the given root.

$\sqrt[3]{-8} = -2$ $\sqrt[3]{-125} = -5$

$\sqrt[3]{x^3} =$ ____________. Can you take a cube root of a negative number and get a real answer? If so, why does it work for a cube root but not a square root?

Examples
Simplify.

4a. $\sqrt[3]{54x^6}$ b. $\sqrt[3]{-40x^4y^{13}}$ c. $\sqrt[3]{250a^8b^{11}}$

How do you simplify the coefficient if the index is 4? If the index is 5?

How do you simplify the exponents if the index is 4? If the index is 5?

Generalize your findings to describe how to simplify the coefficients and exponents for even roots and odd roots.

Examples
Simplify.

5a. $\sqrt[4]{81x^5y^{10}}$ b. $\sqrt[5]{-32x^9y^{11}}$

Quick Quiz

Simplify each radical.

1. $-\sqrt{45}$
2. $\sqrt{8x^3}$
3, $-\sqrt{9x^2y^2}$
4. $\sqrt{\frac{5x^4}{9}}$
5. $\sqrt[3]{-64a^5}$
6. $\sqrt{\frac{196x^{15}y^{10}}{49}}$

Addition and Subtraction with Radicals

What are "**like radicals**"?

When we add like terms, we add ONLY the coefficients. This rule holds true for adding like radicals if we consider the coefficient to be the number in front of the radical.

Combine like terms: $2\sqrt{5}+3\sqrt{5}-8\sqrt{5}=$

The expression $2x\sqrt{5}+2y\sqrt{5}$ cannot be simplified any further even though they have the same index and radicand. Why not?

In some cases, radicals can be simplified to result in like terms.

Given, $4\sqrt{12}+\sqrt{75}-\sqrt{108}$

Simplify each radical. $8\sqrt{3}+5\sqrt{3}-6\sqrt{3}$

Combine like terms. $7\sqrt{3}$

Examples

Simplify each radical to determine if they are "like" radicals. If they are, combine them.

1a. $\sqrt{32x}+\sqrt{18x}$ b. $\sqrt{12}+\sqrt{18}+\sqrt{27}$ c. $\sqrt[3]{5x}-\sqrt[3]{40x}$

d. $x\sqrt{4y^3}-5\sqrt{x^2y^3}$ 2a. $3\sqrt{6}+5\sqrt{6}-\sqrt{6}$ b. $\sqrt{a}+4\sqrt{b}+8\sqrt{a}+3\sqrt{b}$

Quick Quiz

Simplify.

1. $4\sqrt{11}-3\sqrt{11}$
2. $\sqrt{a}+4\sqrt{a}-2\sqrt{a}$
3. $\sqrt{80}+\sqrt{8}-\sqrt{45}+\sqrt{50}$
4. $2\sqrt[3]{128}+5\sqrt[3]{-54}$

Multiplication with Radicals

Recall	Make your own examples to illustrate each.
$\sqrt{a}\cdot\sqrt{b}=\sqrt{a\cdot b}$	Example:
$\sqrt{x^2}=x$	Example:
$\sqrt[3]{x^3}=x$	Example:

Examples

Multiply and simplify. Remember algebraic concepts such as FOIL and conjugate multiplication.

1a. $\sqrt{5}\cdot\sqrt{15}$ b. $5\sqrt{3}\cdot 2\sqrt{6}$ c. $\sqrt{7}(\sqrt{7}-\sqrt{14})$

d. $(3\sqrt{7}-2)(\sqrt{7}+3)$ e. $(1-\sqrt{3x+4})^2$ f. $(5-\sqrt[3]{4})(5+\sqrt[3]{4})$

2a. $6\sqrt{3}(\sqrt{3}+2\sqrt{7})$ b. $(\sqrt{x}+8)(\sqrt{x}-4)$

Quick Quiz

Multiply the radical expressions and simplify.

1. $\sqrt{2}(\sqrt{3}-\sqrt{6})$
2. $(3+\sqrt{2})(5-\sqrt{2})$
3. $2\sqrt[3]{72}\cdot\sqrt[3]{3}$
4. $(\sqrt{5}+2\sqrt{2})^2$

Rationalizing Denominators

An expression with a radical in the denominator is NOT simplified. Any irrational denominators must be rationalized.

What does it mean to **rationalize a denominator**? What is the ultimate goal?

Steps to **rationalize a denominator**.

Denominator is a **monomial**.	1. Simplify the monomial in the denominator. 2. Use the index to determine how many factors are needed to make the radicand perfect. 3. Multiply the numerator and denominator by a radical with those factors. 4. Reduce.
Denominator is a **binomial**.	1. Simplify the binomial. 2. Multiply the numerator and denominator by the conjugate of the denominator. 3. Reduce.

Examples

Simplify.

1a. $\frac{5}{\sqrt{3}}$

b. $\frac{4}{\sqrt{x}}$

c. $\frac{3}{7\sqrt{2}}$

d. $\frac{\sqrt{7}}{\sqrt{8}}$

e. $\frac{x}{\sqrt[3]{9}}$

Let's take a look at a few more examples of the index being greater than 2.

Example $\frac{5}{\sqrt[3]{2}}$ The goal is to create a perfect cube in the denominator. The index is 3, so three identical factors are required to create a perfect cube and for the factors to "come out" of the radical. There is currently one 2, so two 2's are needed to get a total of three. ($2 \cdot 2 \cdot 2$ is a perfect cube, 8.) $\frac{5}{\sqrt[3]{2}} \cdot \frac{\sqrt[3]{2 \cdot 2}}{\sqrt[3]{2 \cdot 2}} = \frac{5\sqrt[3]{4}}{\sqrt[3]{8}} = \frac{5\sqrt[3]{4}}{2}$	Example $\frac{5}{\sqrt[4]{xy^2z^6}}$ The goal is to create a perfect "fourth" in the denominator. The index is 4, so four identical factors are required for factors to "come out" of the radical. In this example three more x's, two more y's, and two more z's are needed. Remember that powers need to be a multiple of the index. $\frac{5}{\sqrt[4]{xy^2z^6}} \cdot \frac{\sqrt[4]{x^3y^2z^2}}{\sqrt[4]{x^3y^2z^2}} = \frac{5\sqrt[4]{x^3y^2z^2}}{\sqrt[4]{x^4y^4z^8}} = \frac{5\sqrt[4]{x^3y^2z^2}}{xyz^2}$

Now let's look at rationalizing fractions with a **binomial** in the denominator. We must multiply the numerator and the denominator by the **conjugate** of the denominator.

The conjugate of $4 - \sqrt{2}$ is: The conjugate of $3 + \sqrt{5}$ is:

The conjugate is **NOT** the same as the opposite. The opposite of a binomial changes the signs of both terms. The conjugate changes only the sign of the second term.

Why does multiplying by the conjugate remove the radicals?

Examples

Simplify.

2a. $\frac{2}{4-\sqrt{2}}$ b. $\frac{31}{6+\sqrt{5}}$ c. $\frac{1}{\sqrt{7}-\sqrt{2}}$

d. $\frac{6}{1+\sqrt{x}}$ e. $\frac{x-y}{\sqrt{x}-\sqrt{y}}$ 3. $\frac{74}{9+\sqrt{7}}$

Quick Quiz

Rationalize the denominators. Reduce if possible.

1. $\frac{5}{\sqrt{2}}$ 2. $\sqrt{\frac{3}{8}}$ 3. $\frac{8}{\sqrt[3]{36}}$

4. $\frac{3}{1+\sqrt{2}}$ 5. $\frac{8}{2\sqrt{x}-3}$ 6. $\frac{\sqrt{2}+4}{5-\sqrt{2}}$

Equations with Radicals

Steps to solve equations with radicals.

1.

2.

3.

4.

5.

Be careful when squaring a binomial. A common mistake is evaluating $(a + b)^2$ as $a^2 + b^2$. Why is this incorrect and what does $(a + b)^2$ equal if expanded?

When both sides of an equation are raised to a power, we may introduce answers that are not actually solutions to the original equation. These solutions are called ________________________ solutions.

Why does raising both sides of an equation to a power create solutions that may not work in the original? In the case of radical equations, what type of answers might work outside the radical world but not work inside the radical world?

Examples

Solve and check.

1a. $\sqrt{x-9} = 2$ b. $\sqrt{x^2 + 13} = 7$ c. $\sqrt{3x + 13} + 3 = 2x$

d. $\sqrt{x+1} = -3$ 2. $\sqrt{5y + 6} = 3y - 2$

Steps to solve equations that include more than one radical term.

1. Isolate one radical.
2. Raise both sides of the equation to the appropriate power. (Indicated by the index.)
3. Isolate the remaining radical, raise it to the appropriate power, and solve for the variable.

Examples

Solve and check.

3a. $\sqrt{x+4} = \sqrt{3x-2}$

b. $\sqrt{2x-14} - \sqrt{x} = 1$

4a. $\sqrt[3]{2x+1} + 1 = 3$

b. $\sqrt[3]{3x+1} + 4 = 2$

Quick Quiz

Solve the following radical equations. Check your solution.

1. $\sqrt{7+3x} = 5$

2. $\sqrt[3]{4+6y} = 4$

3. $\sqrt[3]{10x+16} - 1 = 3$

4. $\sqrt{3x+1} = 1 - \sqrt{x}$

Complex Numbers

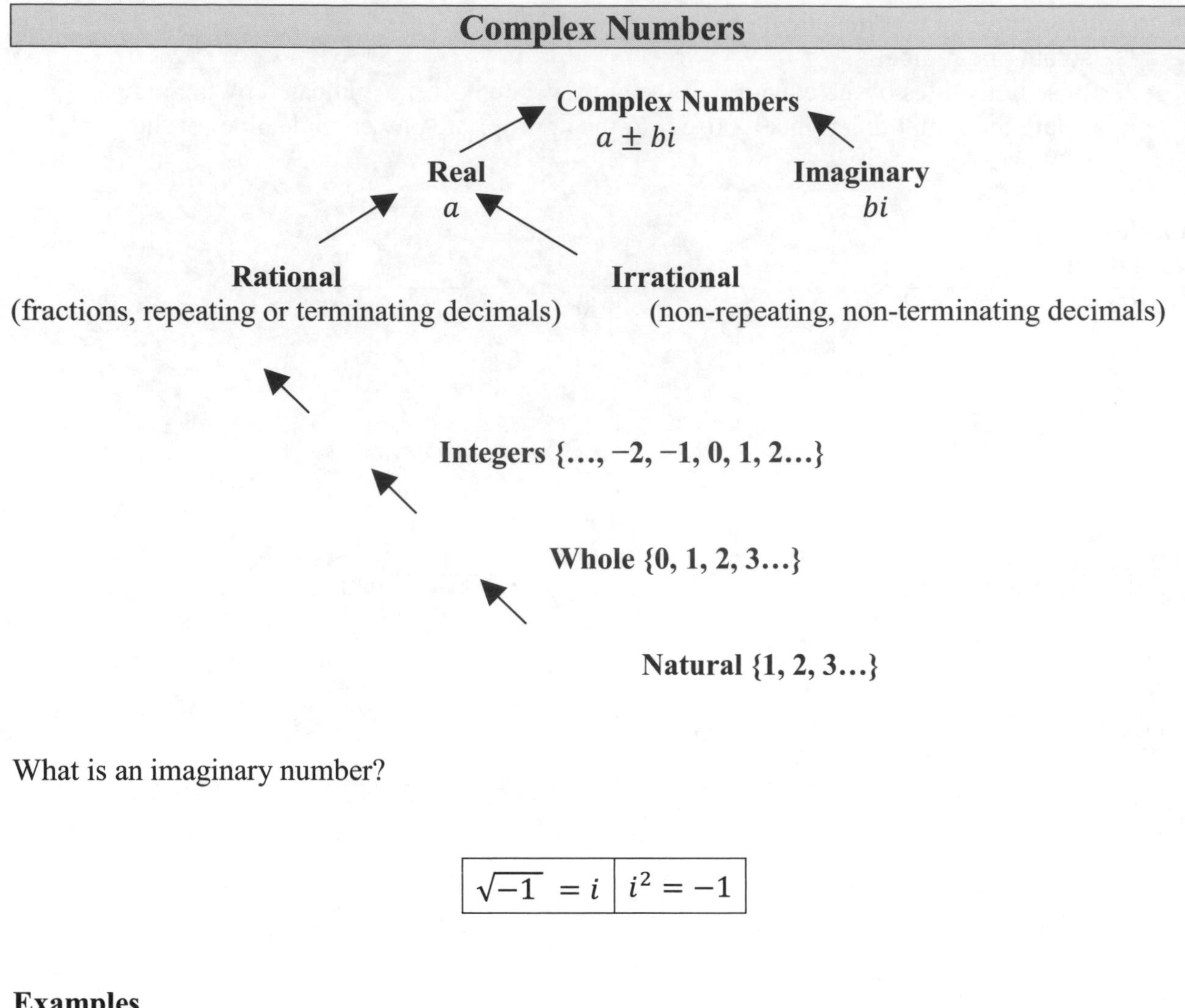

What is an imaginary number?

$\sqrt{-1} = i$	$i^2 = -1$

Examples
Simplify.

1a. $\sqrt{-25}$ b. $\sqrt{-36}$ c. $\sqrt{-24}$ d. $\sqrt{-45}$

Make sure you are not putting the i under the radical sign. To avoid confusion, the "i" is often placed in front of the radical.
We have discussed in the past that an even root of a negative number is NOT REAL. Now we know where to classify these values. They are **imaginary** numbers.

Define **complex numbers** and identify the real and imaginary parts of an expression.

Examples

2. Identify the real part and the imaginary part of each complex number:

	Standard form	Real part	Imaginary part
$4 - 2i$			
$\frac{5+2i}{3}$			
7			
$-\sqrt{3}\,i$			

When we add like terms, we add ONLY the coefficients. This principle applies to imaginary numbers as well if the "i" is treated as a variable until the end at which point it needs to be evaluated if possible.

$(2 + 3i) + (9 - 8i) =$

Remember to distribute the negative in front of a binomial:

$(5 - 2i) - (6 + 7i) =$

Examples

Find the sum or difference and simplify.

3a. $(6 - 2i) + (1 - 2i)$

b. $(-8 - \sqrt{2}i) - (-8 + \sqrt{2}i)$

c. $(\sqrt{3} - 2i) + (1 + \sqrt{5}i)$ What is the real part and the imaginary part of this sum?

Remember when we multiply like bases, we add their exponents. This principle applies to imaginary numbers as well if the "i" is treated as a variable until the end at which point it needs to be evaluated if possible.

Examples

Multiply and simplify.

4a. $3i \cdot 4i$

b. $5i(3 + 2i)$

c. $(3 + 2i)(4 + 5i)$

Even radicals with negative radicands.

When we have radicals that include taking the root of a negative number, this indicates the presence of imaginary numbers, **we must "take out the *i*'s first"** before we continue work on evaluating the radical. Consider the $\sqrt{-\#}$ as $\sqrt{-1 \cdot \#}$ and the $\sqrt{-1} = i$.

	$3\sqrt{-4} + 2\sqrt{-4}\,(3\sqrt{-9}\,)$
Step 1: Take the square root of each −1 in the radicand.	$3i\sqrt{4} + 2i\sqrt{4}\,(3i\sqrt{9}\,)$
Step 2: Simplify the square root of the remaining radicand.	$3(2i) + 2(2i) \cdot 3(3i)$
Step 3: Apply order of operations.	$6i + 4i(9i) = 6i + 36i^2$
Step 4: Simplify. Evaluate powers of "*i*".	$6i + 36(-1) = 6i - 36$
Step 5: Write in standard form.	$-36 + 6i$

	$2\sqrt{-3}(\sqrt{-3} + 5\sqrt{-2})$
Step 1-2: Simplify square root with attention to – radicand.	$2i\sqrt{3}(i\sqrt{3} + 5i\sqrt{2})$
Step 3: Apply order of operations. (Distribute.)	$2i^2\sqrt{9} + 10i^2\sqrt{6}$
Step 4: Simplify. Evaluate powers of "*i*".	$6i^2 + 10i^2\sqrt{6} = 6(-1) + 10(-1)\sqrt{6}$
Step 5: Write in standard form.	$-6 - 10\sqrt{6}$

Quick Quiz

Perform the indicated operation. Leave your answer in standard form.

1. $(2 + 3i) - (-7 - i)$

2. $(-7 + \sqrt{-36}\,) + (4 + \sqrt{-16}\,)$

3. $2i(3 + i)$

4. $(5 + 7i)(6 - 10i)$

Applications: The Pythagorean Theorem

State the **Pythagorean Theorem** and draw the illustration to reference.

Something to think about…
Where did the Pythagorean Theorem come from? Who developed it?

Examples

Draw and label right triangles to demonstrate the problem and apply the theorem to solve.

1. Show that a triangle with sides of 3 in., 4 in., and 5 in. must be a right triangle.

2. Find the length of the hypotenuse for a right triangle with legs 1 cm long and 3 cm long.

3. Find the length of the unknown leg of a right triangle which has one leg of 13 inches and the hypotenuse of 20 inches.

4. A guy wire is attached to the top of a telephone pole and anchored in the ground 20 feet from the base of the pole. If the pole is 40 feet high, what is the length of the guy wire?

Quick Quiz

Draw and label right triangles to demonstrate the problem and apply the theorem to solve.

1. Find the length of the hypotenuse.

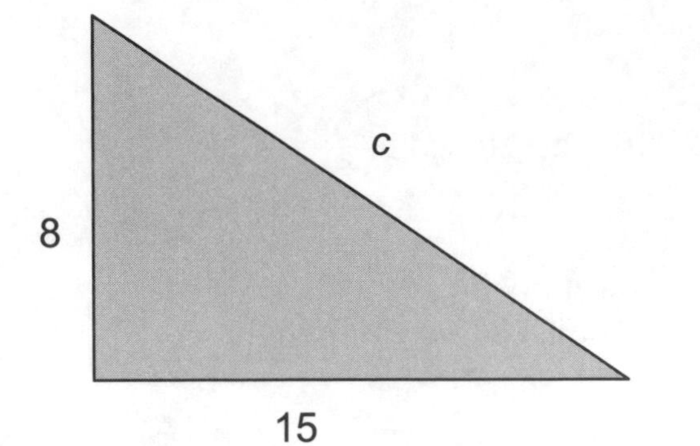

2. Find the length of leg b.

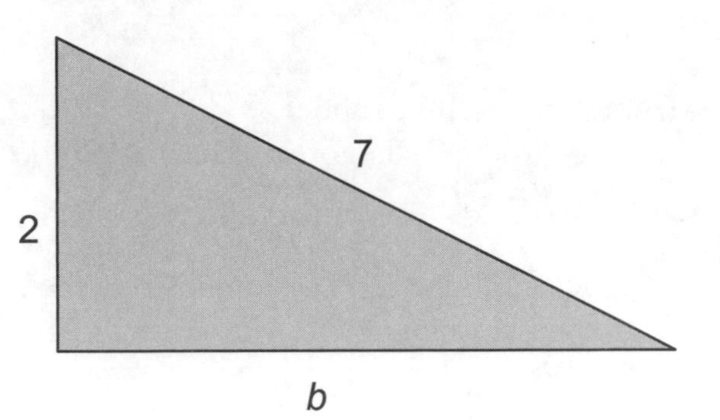

3. The bottom of a ladder is placed 6 yards from a tree. If the ladder is 10 yards long, what is the height of the tallest branch in the tree that the ladder can reach?

Applications: Distance Formula and Midpoint Formula

What is the **distance formula**? Identify the meaning of each variable.

When the formula is applied, the solution will always be what type of number?

How is the Pythagorean theorem used to find the distance between two points?

Examples

Find the distance between the two points:

1a. $(-2,7)$ and $(3,4)$

b. $(-6,-8)$ and $(-4,-5)$

2. Use the distance formula and Pythagorean theorem to determine whether or not the triangle with vertices at $A(-5,-1)$, $B(2,1)$, and $C(0,7)$is a right triangle.

What is the **midpoint formula**? Identify the meaning of each variable.

When the formula is applied, the solution will always be in what form?

Examples

3. Find the coordinates of the midpoint of the line segment joining the two points $P(-4,6)$ and $Q(1,2)$. Sketch a graph to represent what you have found.

Quick Quiz

Find the distance between the following points.

1. $(4,-1),(3,-10)$

Find the coordinates of the midpoint of the line segment joining the two points.

2. $(0,-6),(-2,10)$

Find the perimeter of the triangle determined by the given points.

3. $A(-5,0),\ B(3,4),\ C(0,0)$

Vocabulary Check

Define each of the following terms in your own words, providing examples as necessary to clarify the term.

Complex number

Conjugate

Extraneous solution

Hypotenuse

Imaginary number

Like radicals

Principal square root

Pure imaginary number

Radical expression

Concept Review

Answer the following questions as completely as possible in your own words. Make sure to get the big points of each with key steps involved.

1. When an exponent is a fraction, what does it mean?

2. When an exponent is negative, what does it mean? How do you make it positive?

3. What are the power rules?

4. $(\text{Any nonzero number})^0 =$

5. What are the two properties of nth roots?

6. What is the relationship between radicals and powers?

7. In the real number system, under what conditions can the radicand be negative? Under what conditions can it not be negative?

8. When is a radical considered to be in simplest form?

9. How do you rationalize a denominator containing a monomial?

10. How do you rationalize a denominator containing a binomial?

11. How do you solve a radical equation?

12. What must you check once you have found a solution?

13. What is the standard form of a complex number?

14. How do you find the distance between two points?

15. How do you find the midpoint between two points?

16. What are the following theorems or formulas and how are they used?
    a. Pythagorean Theorem

    b. Distance Formula

    c. Midpoint Formula

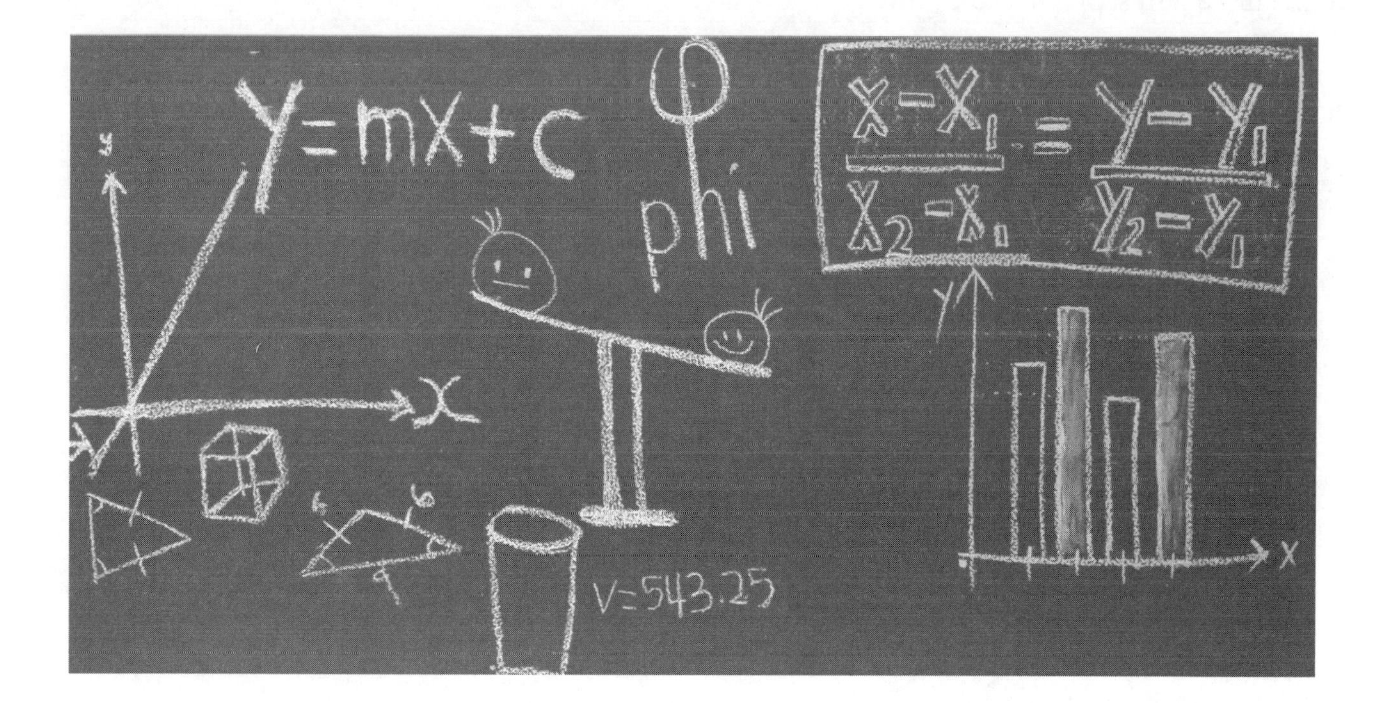

Unit 9

Functions, Quadratic Equations, and Parabolas

Functions and Function Notation

Define these terms.

Relation

Domain *D*

Range *R*

Examples

1. Find the domain and range.

a. $g = \{(5,7),(6,2),(6,3),(-1\ 2)\}$

Domain: Range:

b. $f = \{(-1,1),(1,5),(0,3)\}$

Domain: Range:

2. Use the graph given to identify the domain and range of each relation. Write the solution using interval notation.

a. Domain: Range:

b. Domain: Range:

Define **function**.

Rewrite this definition in your own words.

3. Is it a function? Why or why not?

a. $s = \{\ (2,3),(1,6),(2,4),(0,-1)\}$

b. $t = \{(1,5),(3,5),(\sqrt{2},5),(-1,5),(-4,5)\}$

Describe the **vertical line test**.

Examples

4. Use the vertical line test to determine whether or not the graph is a function. Then list the domain and range of each graph given.

a. Is it a function? Domain: Range:

b. Is it a function? Domain: Range:

c. Is it a function? Domain: Range:

d. Is it a function? Domain: Range:

Define **linear function**.

Why does the text say, "nonvertical" lines represent functions? What makes a vertical line NOT a function?

To find the restrictions on a domain, we must find values that make the denominator zero.

Examples

5. Find the domain for the function $y = \frac{2x+1}{x-5}$.

Define **radical function**.

The domain of such a function depends on the ______________.

1.

2.

If the index is even, **why** must the radicand be greater than or equal to zero?

Examples

6. Determine the domain.

a. $y = \sqrt{2x+3}$

b. $y = \sqrt[3]{x-7}$

Function Notation

$y = -3x + 2$ can be written in function notation as ______________.

$f(4) =$ ______________

The ordered pair $(4, -10)$ can be written as $(4,$____$)$ if function notation is used.

Examples

7. For the function $g(x) = 4x + 5,$ find the following.
   a. $g(2)$ b. $g(-1)$ c. $g(0)$ d. $g(x-1)$

8. For the function $h(x) = x^2 - 3x + 2,$ find the following.
   a. $h(4)$ b. $h(0)$ c. $h(-3)$ d. $h(x^2)$

9. Complete the table for each function.
   a. $f(x) = \sqrt[3]{x-7}$ b. $f(x) = 3\sqrt{x}$

x	$f(x)$
7	
6	
−1	

x	$f(x)$
0	
4	
6	

Quick Quiz

1. $T = \{(1, 2), (4, 7), (1, 7), (8, 2)\}$
   a. List the domain. b. List the range.
   c. Is the relation a function? Why or why not.

2. Evaluate the function $f(x) = x^2 + 7$ for the given values.
   a. $f(4)$ b. $f(-3)$

3. Determine and write the domain of each function using interval notation.
   a. $y = -8x + 1$ b. $y = \frac{2}{x+2}$ c. $y = \sqrt{x+8}$

Solving Quadratic Equations: The Square Root Method

State the **zero-factor property**.

What is a **quadratic equation**?

What is the standard form of a quadratic? (What do the coefficients have to be?)

Why must "a" be a number other than zero?

Steps to solve quadratic equations by factoring.

1.

2.

3.

4.

What is the maximum number of solutions a quadratic equation can have? What part of the equation gives this information?

Examples

1. Solve by factoring.

a. $x^2 - 15x = -50$

b. $3x^2 + 48 = 24x$

What is it called when an equation results in the same value for both solutions?

State the **square root property**.

How can the square root property be applied to solving quadratic equations? What condition(s) must be met to apply this property?

What happens if you take the square root of a negative number?

Examples

2. Solve using the square root property.

   a. $(y+4)^2 = 8$

   b. $x^2 = -25$

Quick Quiz

Solve for the variable. Simplify any radical expressions.

1. $5x^2 = 60$

2. $(x+2)^2 = -25$

3. $(x-2)^2 = \frac{1}{16}$

4. $(2x+1)^2 = 48$

Solving Quadratic Equations: Completing the Square

Each of these trinomials is a perfect square. Factor each trinomial.

$x^2 - 8x + 16$ $\qquad$ $x^2 + 20x + 100$

The quadratic equation $ax^2 + bx + c = 0$ is a perfect square if

$$\left(\frac{1}{2}b\right)^2 = c$$

Examples

1. Find $\left(\frac{1}{2}b\right)^2$ to complete the perfect square. Then factor the new trinomial.

a. $x^2 + 10x$ $\qquad$ b. $x^2 - 7x$

Steps to solve a quadratic equation by completing the square.

1.

2.

3.

4.

Examples

2. Solve by completing the square.

a. $x^2 - 8x = 25$ $\qquad$ b. $3x^2 + 6x - 15 = 0$

c. $-2x^2 - 2x + 7 = 0$

d. $x^2 - 2x + 13 = 0$

Quick Quiz

Complete the square.

1. $x^2 + 12x +$ ______ $= (x +$ ____$)^2$

2. $2x^2 - 16x$

Solve by completing the square.

3. $x^2 + 8x + 2 = 0$

4. $x^2 + x - 3 = 0$

The Quadratic Formula

What is the **Quadratic Formula**?

What is its purpose?

Memorize this formula. Notice the fraction bar goes all the way across.

If the leading coefficient of a quadratic equation is negative, how can we make it positive?

Examples

1. Solve each equation using the quadratic formula.

   a. $x^2 - 5x + 3 = 0$ b. $7x^2 - 2x + 1 = 0$ c. $\frac{3}{4}x^2 - \frac{1}{2}x = \frac{1}{3}$

Describe and demonstrate the correct way to reduce the solution $\frac{4+2\sqrt{3}}{2}$.

Examples

2. Solve the cubic equation first by factoring and then using the quadratic formula.
   $2x^3 - 10x^2 + 6x = 0$

What is a **discriminant**?

What does it describe?

Discriminant: $b^2 - 4ac$	**Nature of solutions**
If $D > 0$ and is not perfect	
If D is a perfect square	
If $D = 0$	
If $D < 0$	

Examples

3. Find the discriminant to determine the nature of the solutions for each of the quadratic equations.

a. $3x^2 + 11x - 7 = 0$

b. $x^2 + 6x + 9 = 0$

c. $x^2 + 1 = 0$

d. $x^2 + 6x + 8 = 0$

4a. Determine the value(s) for c such that $x^2 + 8x + c = 0$ will have one real solution.

b. Determine the value(s) for a such that $ax^2 - 8x + 4 = 0$ will have two nonreal solutions.

Quick Quiz

Find the discriminant and determine the number of solutions and whether the solutions are real or non-real.

1. $x^2 - 8x + 16 = 0$

2. $5x^2 + 8x + 3 = 0$

3. $-3x^2 = -3x + 2$

Solve for the variable using the quadratic formula.

1. $x^2 - 4x - 1 = 0$

2. $9x^2 + 12x - 2 = -6$

3. $(2x + 1)(x + 3) = 2x + 6$

Applications: Quadratic Equations

Describe strategies you can use to help write the equation that relates to the application problem.

1.

2.

3.

4.

State the **Pythagorean Theorem** and draw the illustration to reference.

Something to think about…
Where did the Pythagorean Theorem come from? Who developed it?

Examples

1. The length of a rectangular field is 6 meters longer than its width. If a diagonal foot path stretching from one corner of the field to the opposite corner is 30 meters long, what are the dimensions of the field?

State the **formula for projectiles**.

Examples

2. A bullet is fired straight up from ground level with a muzzle velocity of 320 feet per second.
   a. When will the bullet hit the ground?

   b. When will the bullet be 1200 feet above the ground?

3. A rectangular sheet of copper is 6 in. longer than it is wide. Three inch by three inch squares are cut from each corner and the sides are folded up to form an open box. If the box has a volume of 336 inches cubed, what are the dimensions of the original sheet of copper?

4. The members of a bowling club were going to rent a bus to drive them to a tournament at a total cost of $2420, which was to be divided equally among the members. At the last minute, two of the members decided to drive their own cars. The cost to the remaining members increased $11 each. How many members rode the bus?

5. Working for a janitorial service, a woman and her daughter can clean a building in 4 hours. If the daughter were to do the job by herself, she would take 6 hours longer than her mother would take. How long would it take her mother to clean the building without the daughter's help?

Quick Quiz

1. Jack and Diane are decorating a nursery room for their baby, who will be born in a few months. Working together, they can completely decorate the nursery in 4 hours. Working alone, it would take Diane 6 hours longer to decorate the nursery than it would take Jack. How long would it take Jack and Diane to decorate the nursery by themselves?

   a. Use the table to set up a rational equation to describe the situation. Use the variable x to represent the time it takes Jack to decorate the nursery by himself.

Person(s)	Time of Work (in Hours)	Part of Work Done in 1 Hour
Jack		
Diane		
Together		

   b. Solve the equation from part a.

   c. Which solution from part b. makes sense in the context of the situation? Explain your reasoning.

   d. Use the answer from part c. to answer the question from the problem statement.

2. Lisa traveled to a college that is located 200 miles from the city where she works to train customers on how to use the courseware that her company sells. Due to a traffic jam, her average speed returning was 10 miles per hour less than her average speed going to the college. The total travel time to and from the college was 9 hours. What was Lisa's average speed going to the college?

   a. Use the table to set up a rational equation to describe the situation. Use the variable x to represent the average speed going to the college. (Hint: The sum of the times that it took Lisa to travel to and from the college is 9 hours.)

	Distance (d)	÷	Rate (r)	=	Time
Going					
Returning					

b. Solve the equation from part a. Round your answer to the nearest tenth.

c. Which solution from part b. makes sense in the context of the situation? Explain your reasoning.

d. Use the answer from part c. to answer the question from the problem statement.

3. A landscaper was given the task to create a triangular flower garden in the corner of an office building. The landscaper has 12 feet of low fencing to use as a border along one side of the garden. The final garden will have the shape shown in the figure. The landscaper needs to know the remaining side lengths of the triangle to determine the area he will need to cover with fresh topsoil.

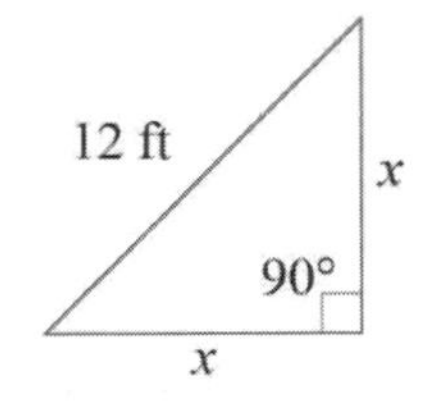

a. Use the Pythagorean Theorem to set up an equation which describes the relationship between the side lengths of the flower garden.

b. Solve the equation from part a. for the variable. Round your answer(s) to the nearest tenth.

c. Which solution from part b. makes sense in the context of the situation? Explain your reasoning.

d. Use the answer from part c. to determine the area that the landscaper will need to cover with topsoil.

4. A farmer fenced in a 198-square-meter portion of his field with 58 meters of fencing. What are the length and width of the field? (Hint: The length plus the width is equal to half of the perimeter.)

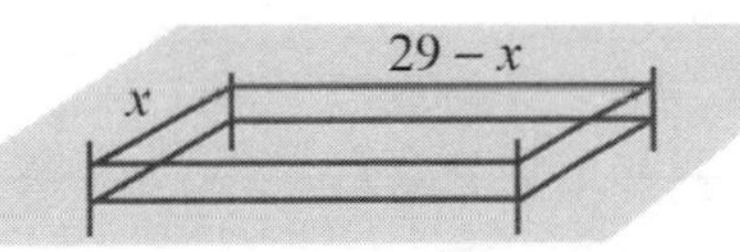

a. Write an equation to express the area of the field.

b. Solve the equation from part a. for the variable.

5. Use the answer from part b. to determine the length and width of the field.

Graphs of Quadratic Functions

The graph of every quadratic function is a ____________________.

Why don't horizontal parabolas represent a function?

Forms of Quadratic Functions
$\boldsymbol{y = a(x - h)^2 + k}$ is a variation of $\boldsymbol{y = x^2}$
and represents a function that has moved away from the origin or has been elongated or widened.
Each letter a, h, and k represents a shift in the original $y = x^2$.

Sketch the parabola $\boldsymbol{y = x^2}$.
Identify

- Values of a, h, and k
- Location of the vertex
- Direction of opening

Given a parabola in standard form: $y = a(x - h)^2 + k$, identify what information can be drawn from the function.

Given	Describe what the given represents or what information it provides about the parabola.
(h, k)	
If $a > 0$	
If $a < 0$	
As $\lvert a \rvert$ increases	
As $\lvert a \rvert$ decreases	
The line $x = h$	
If $(x - h)^2$, then h is positive	
If $(x + h)^2$, then h is negative	
If k is positive	
If k is negative	

Examples

For each function, identify the values of a, h, and k. Graph the function and identify the line of symmetry, vertex, domain, and range.

1. $y = 2x^2 - 3$

   Hint:

   $y = 2(x - 0)^2 - 3$ $\quad a = 2;\ \ h = 0;\ \ k = -3$

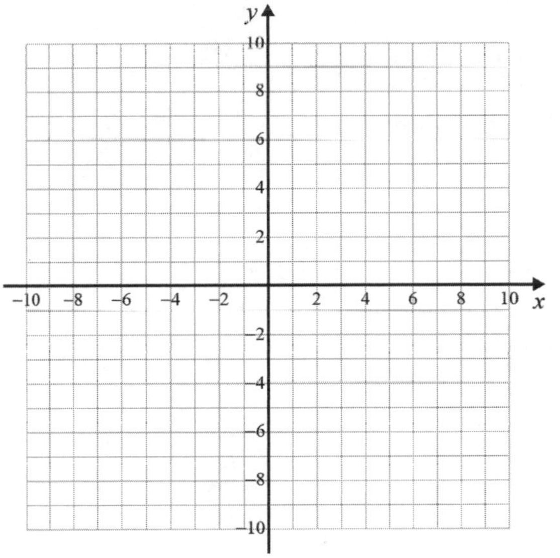

line of symmetry:

vertex:

domain:

range:

2. $y = -\left(x - \frac{5}{2}\right)^2$

$a =$ ________ $h =$ ________ $k =$ ________

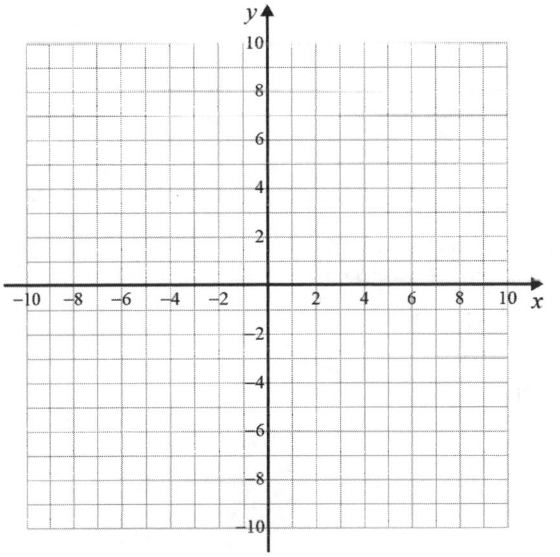

line of symmetry:

vertex:

domain:

range:

3a. $y = -2(x - 3)^2 + 5$

$a =$ ________ $h =$ ________ $k =$ ________

line of symmetry:

vertex:

domain:

range:

y: 10, 8, 6, 4, 2, −2, −4, −6, −8, −10
x: −10, −8, −6, −4, −2, 2, 4, 6, 8, 10

3b. $y = \left(x + \frac{1}{2}\right)^2 - 2$

$a =$ ________ $h =$ ________ $k =$ ________

line of symmetry:

vertex:

domain:

range:

y: 10, 8, 6, 4, 2, −2, −4, −6, −8, −10
x: −10, −8, −6, −4, −2, 2, 4, 6, 8, 10

Quick Quiz

Graph the following functions. For each graph determine the line of symmetry, vertex, domain, and range.

1. $y = 2x^2$

2. $y = -(x + 1)^2$

3. $y = 4(x - 5)^2 + 1$

Quadratic Functions: Completing the Square and Applications

Steps for rewriting a quadratic equation in standard form to the form $y = a(x - h)^2 + k$ by completing the square.

1. Factor out the leading coefficient from the first two terms, separating the constant.
2. Determine the value needed to complete the square $\left(\frac{1}{2}b\right)^2$, then add and subtract this value inside of parentheses. (Net gain of 0.)
3. Remove the negative value from parentheses – remember to multiply by the leading coefficient.
4. Factor the trinomial as a perfect square, and add the last two terms together.

How can you find the **vertex** of a quadratic function in standard form?

Once you find the vertex, how do you then write the equation of the **line of symmetry**?

Examples

1. Write each expression in the form $a(x - h)^2 + k$ by completing the square.

   a. $x^2 + 2x + 6$

   b. $-2x^2 + 8x - 1$

Steps to graph a quadratic function.

1.

2.

3.

4.

What is also referred to as the **zeros of the function** and how is it found?

What does it mean if the x-intercepts are non-real numbers?

If the x-intercept(s) are found when y=0, how is the y-intercept found?

Examples

2. Graph $y = x^2 - 8x + 7$ by rewriting the function and identifying a, h, and k.

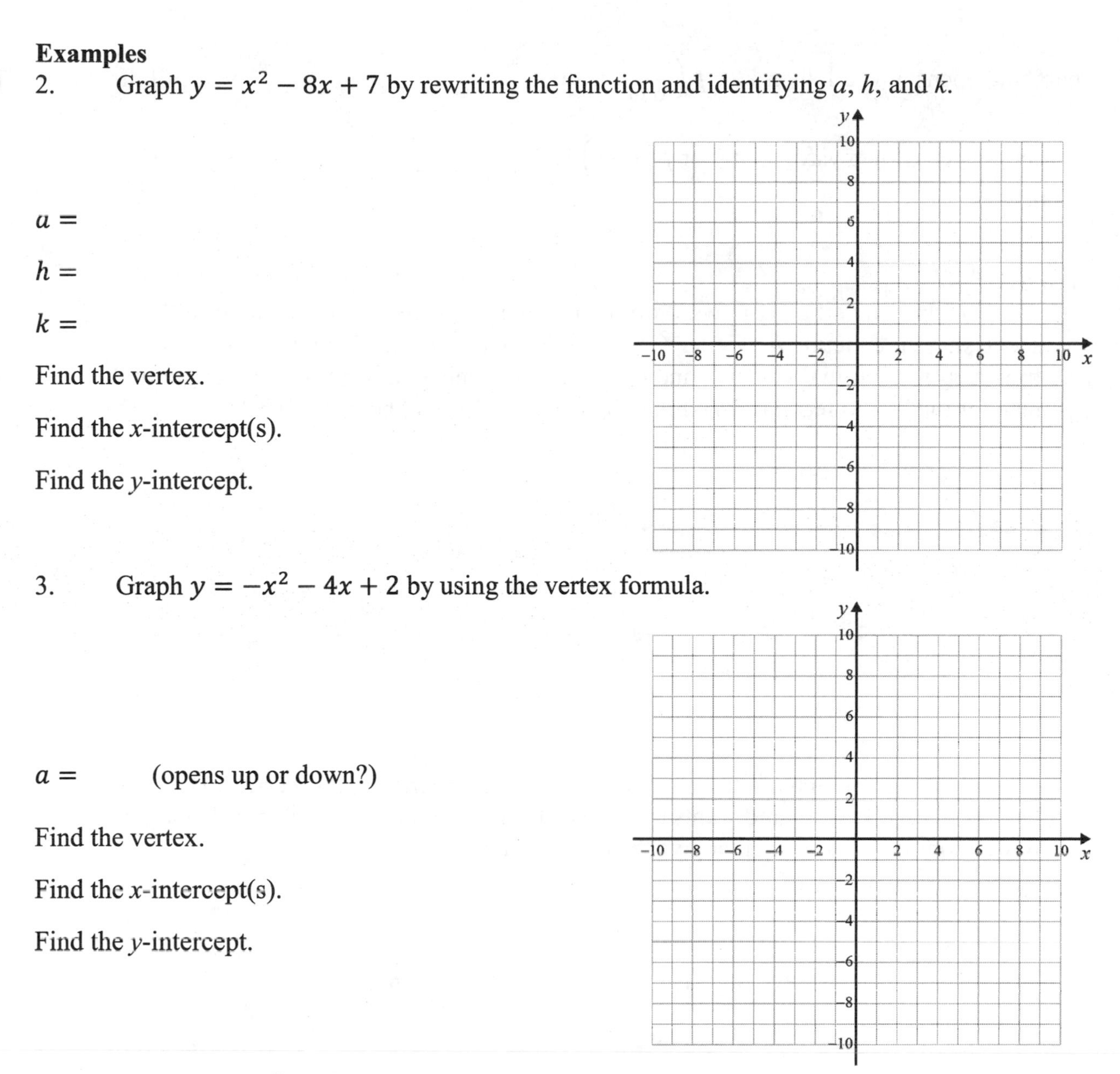

$a =$

$h =$

$k =$

Find the vertex.

Find the x-intercept(s).

Find the y-intercept.

3. Graph $y = -x^2 - 4x + 2$ by using the vertex formula.

$a =$ (opens up or down?)

Find the vertex.

Find the x-intercept(s).

Find the y-intercept.

4. Graph $y = 2x^2 - 6x + 5$ by using the vertex formula.

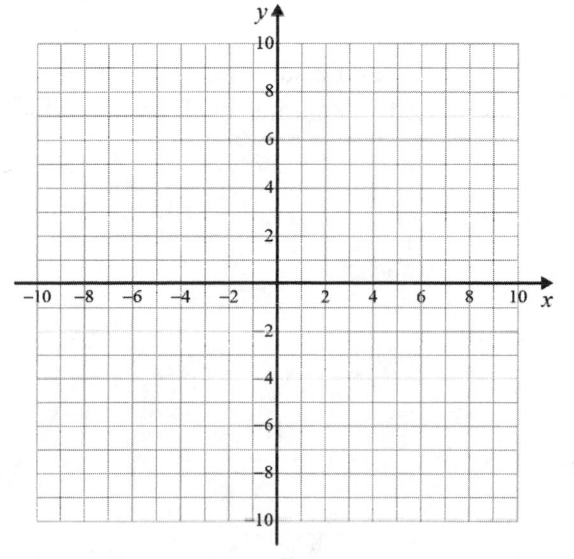

$a =$ (opens up or down?)

Find the vertex.

Find the x-intercept(s).

Find the y-intercept.

If a parabola opens upward, then k or $f\left(-\frac{b}{2a}\right)$ is the ______________________ value of the function.

If a parabola opens downward, then k or $f\left(-\frac{b}{2a}\right)$ is the ______________________ value of the function.

Examples

5a. A ball is thrown vertically upward from the ground with an initial velocity of 64 ft per sec. Using the function $h = -16t^2 + v_0t + h_0$, where h is the height of the object after time t, v_0 is the initial velocity, and h_0 is the initial height, determine how long it will take for the ball to reach its maximum height and what that height will be.

b. A rancher is going to build three sides of a rectangular corral next to a river. He has 240 feet of fencing and wants to enclose the maximum area possible. What are the dimensions of the fencing that give the corral its maximum area?

c. A video game sales person estimates that by charging x dollars for each game, he can sell $120 - x$ games each week. What price will give him maximum sales revenue?

Quick Quiz

Rewrite each function in the form $y = a(x - h)^2 + k$, and then find the x-intercept(s), y-intercept, and vertex of each quadratic equation. Graph the equation.

1. $y = x^2 - 4x + 5$

2. $2x^2 - 2x = y + 4$

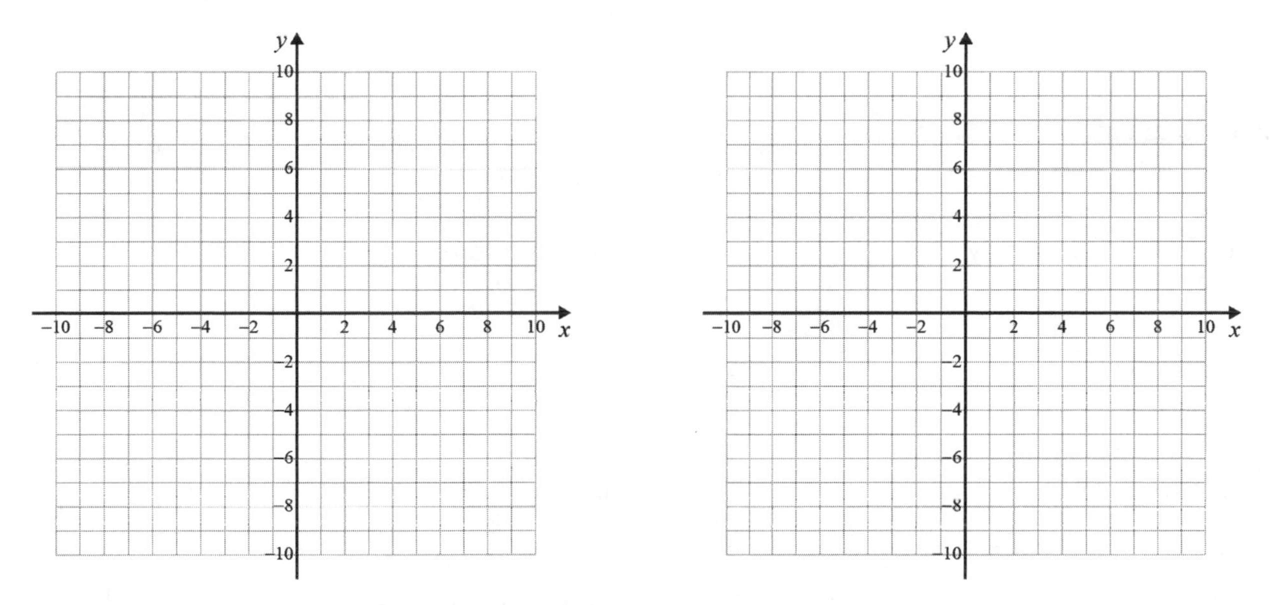

Using the vertex formula, find the vertex of each quadratic equation.

3. $y = x^2 - 8x + 5$

4. $y + \frac{7}{2} = 2x^2 - 12x$

Solve.

5. The perimeter of a rectangle is 72 yards. What are the dimensions of the rectangle with maximum area?

Vocabulary Check

Define each of the following terms in your own words, providing examples as necessary to clarify the term.

Discriminant

Domain

Function

Functional notation

Line (or axis) of symmetry

Linear function

Projectile formula

Pythagorean Theorem

Quadratic formula

Quadratic function

Radical function

Range

Relation

Square root property

Vertex

Work formula

Zero-factor property

Zeros of a quadratic function

Concept Review

Answer the following questions as completely as possible in your own words. Make sure to get the big points of each with key steps involved.

1. How do you find the domain and range of a relation?

2. What is the vertical line test and what is it used for?

3. How do you evaluate a function written using functional notation?

4. How do you solve quadratic equations by factoring?

5. How do you solve quadratic equations using the square root property?

6. How do you solve quadratic equations by completing the square?

7. How do you use the quadratic formula to solve a quadratic equation?

8. How does the discriminant tell you what type of solutions you will have?

9. How can you tell whether the vertex is the minimum or maximum?

10. Given a quadratic function, how do you find the following:

    a. vertex

    b. axis of symmetry

    c. y-intercept

    d. x-intercept(s)

    e. domain and range

11. How do you graph a quadratic function?

Notes

Notes

Notes

Notes

Notes

Notes

Notes

Notes